LEARNING OBJECTIVES FOR INDIVIDUALIZED INSTRUCTION

MATHEMATICS

Westinghouse Learning Press
Division of Westinghouse Learning Corporation

Library of Congress Card Catalog Number 75-23425

ISBN 0-88250-778-8 (Softcover Edition)
ISBN 0-88250-773-7 (Hardcover Edition)

Westinghouse Learning Press
770 Lucerne Drive
Sunnyvale, California 94086

Division of Westinghouse Learning Corporation
New York, New York 10017

Printed in the United States of America

Text set in 10 point Zenith with display
lines in 13 point Goudy Heavyface

Cover design and art by Steven Jacobs Design,
Palo Alto, California

Editorial and production by Westinghouse
Learning Press, Sunnyvale, California

Composition by Typothetae, Palo Alto, California

Lithography by George Banta Company,
Menasha, Wisconsin

Contents

Objectives from the following Westinghouse Learning Press publications have been used or adapted with permission of the authors.

Biology: An Individualized Course
Robert N. Hurst, David H. McGaw, Kenneth H. Bush, Curtis L. Smiley

Earth Science: An Individualized Course
Joseph C. Gould, Charles J. Mott, N. Gerald Langford

Algebra: An Individualized Course
Ephraim G. Salins, Russell L. Fleury

American Government: An Individualized Course
Wallace P. Harrison

Sociology: An Individualized Course, First Edition and Revised Edition
Robert A. Butler

Psychology: An Individualized Course, First Edition and Revised Edition
Richard L. Morgan

Economics: An Individualized Course
Dayton Y. Roberts, Alfred J. Furnweger

English Composition: An Individualized Course, First Edition and Revised Edition
Benson R. Schulman

A Curse on Confusion: An Individualized Approach to Clear Writing
Lowell A. Draper

The Relevance of Patterns: An Individualized Approach to Writing Improvement
Lucille M. Thomas

The Relevance of Sound: An Individualized Approach to Phonetic and Structural Analysis
Frances Coolidge

The Relevance of Words: An Individualized Approach to Spelling
David J. Peterson

The Relevance of Listening: An Individualized Course
Harold D. Sartain

AC Circuits/DC Circuits: An Individualized Approach to Electronics
Paul E. Trejo

Toward Instructional Accountability: A Practical Guide to Educational Change
John E. Roueche, Barton R. Herrscher

Computer Programming: An Individualized Course in FORTRAN IV
Carl A. Grame, Daniel J. O'Donnell

Introduction

Westinghouse Learning Corporation has been involved for almost ten years in developing individualized instructional material for kindergarten, elementary school, high school, college, career training, and industry. Since objectives are a basic component of individualized learning, Westinghouse Learning Corporation has necessarily been a leader in formulating objectives.

With increasing demands for accountability in teaching, many teachers and instructors have found a need for objectives to use or to adapt for their courses. Others wanted guidelines so that they could develop their own objectives as they moved toward greater individualization and accountability in teaching.

This set of objectives has been produced to provide learning objectives for an age range quite different from the usual grade levels, particularly for the mature student, who may never have mastered objectives that are ordinarily covered in earlier years. The typical grade-level organization is not appropriate for these students, who may need some very basic elements but are nonetheless ready to explore the disciplines at a comparatively sophisticated level.

Most of these objectives have been used with students, particularly in classes that emphasize individualization as well as in learning centers and resource laboratories that concentrate on a diagnostic and remedial approach to basic skills.

Cognitive Levels

In the first Westinghouse Learning Corporation collection, *Behavioral Objectives*, the keying of objectives to cognitive levels based on Bloom's *Taxonomy of Educational Objectives, Cognitive Domain*, was so successful that this system has been used again, with some adaptations. Determining the cognitive level of objectives necessarily involves a degree of subjectivity, but every effort has been made to reduce subjectivity through use of a chart, listing the verbs that seem appropriate for behavior at the various cognitive levels. Often modifiers of these verbs have had to be added. Where questions arose regarding the cognitive level of the objectives in these volumes, the editors made judgments as to the actual performance involved, based on the following questions that help to define the six basic levels.

I. Are the students asked simply to repeat facts or show that they have memorized something?

II. Do students have to show understanding of the information presented?

III. Must students apply knowledge to a new situation (as in problem solving), or must they make predictions?

IV. Is it necessary to analyze and organize information?

V. Does the objective require combining and presenting information in a new or creative way?

VI. Do students have to draw together several cognitive levels in evaluating the material or in making judgments based on evaluation?

Using these six questions as the framework, the editors developed the chart on pages viii–ix, which lists verbs that have been used for each of the cognitive levels.

A major difficulty in assigning levels arises from the confusion between the *kinds* of cognitive activity and the *content* associated with that activity. For example, to the student in medical school, a large amount of cognitive activity may be of the kind that is often referred to as the lowest level, memorization. Anatomical terms, drug dosages, symptoms, and treatments must be memorized. The content level of this activity is extremely high, but the activity itself remains at level I. A conscious effort has been made in this collection to present objectives that cover a broad spectrum of cognitive levels and content. It is up to the user of these books to transform a given objective to meet either the content or the cognitive level that is appropriate for a particular unit of instruction.

Organization

Beyond the major divisions into four volumes—Language Arts, Mathematics, Science, and Social Science—a broad set of subject classifications has been used. No attempt has been made to provide comprehensive subject coverage, and many objectives in one category are also applicable to another. The comprehensive index provides cross referencing. Although there are subject subdivisions, there is no grade-level designation. When any text is made up of small parts, the constraints of print mean that each item has a fixed position on a page and within a volume—a position that establishes a sequential relationship regardless of whether such a relationship is logical or intentional. Since objectives may potentially be sequenced in many ways, it is important to understand that the arrangement of this collection is not intended to suggest any prescriptive order. In the sections emphasizing skills, there is some natural sequence based on the cumulative nature of some skills, but in subject areas topics may be presented in almost any order.

In *Learning Objectives for Individualized Instruction,* terminal objectives have been established to provide appropriate learning segments. These terminal objectives are numbered and printed in boldface.

Subobjectives, which may be called transitional or enabling objectives, contribute to the mastery of a terminal objective. These transitional objectives may appear as part of more than one terminal objective. Transitional objectives and terminal objectives are both assigned cognitive levels; transitional objectives are never given a higher cognitive level than the terminal objectives with which they are associated.

The Numbering System

Because many instructors wish to use the computer for storage and retrieval of objectives and related test items, each terminal objective has been given a numerical designator. These numbers have been set up as follows. The two digits at the far left indicate a major area: 01, Language Arts; 02, Mathematics; 03, Social Science; 04, Science. Career areas and other major areas can be added, up to 99. The three middle digits have been reserved for subject areas; in this collection numbers have been assigned to subject areas at intervals of five to allow for interpolation of such other subjects as an instructor finds appropriate. The three digits on the right in the numerical designator signify terminal objectives; these have also been spaced at intervals of five so that others may be inserted.

Since courses have not yet been developed in all subject areas, some disciplines are not covered in this collection and there has been no effort to make coverage complete within a subject area. This collection is designed to encourage the instructor to use these volumes as guidelines rather than as a definite set. Every instructor should feel free to add, subtract, and adapt objectives to meet individual, class, and institutional needs.

Levels of Learning Objectives

I KNOWLEDGE	II COMPREHENSION	III APPLICATION
Emphasis: Recall	*Emphasis:* Grasp of meaning, intent, or relationship	*Emphasis:* Applying appropriate principles or generalizations
choose from a list (judgment not involved)	classify	apply
define (give a dictionary definition)	define (in student's own words)	collect information (supply correct equation or formula)
fill in the blank (or complete)	describe	compute
follow directions	explain	construct
identify	express in other terms	convert (in math)
indicate	find (as in math)	draw
label	measure	determine (calculate)
list	paraphrase	demonstrate
locate (on a map or a given document)	put in order	derive
match	recognize	differentiate between
name	rewrite	discuss
select (judgment not involved)	simplify	distinguish between
	suggest	expand
	summarize	express in a discussion
	trace (on a map, chart, etc.)	estimate
	Math	find (implies investigation)
	add (find the sum)	interpret
	balance	investigate
	calculate	illustrate (give examples not previously specified)
	compute (using a given formula)	graph
	divide (find the quotient)	keep records
	factor	locate (information)
	find square root or raise to power	make
	multiply (find the product)	participate
	perform operations on numbers	perform (except in math or in public)
	subtract (find the difference)	plan
		predict (from known factors)
		prepare
		present
		prove (in math)
		solve (problems expressed in words)
		use
		trace (development, history, process)
		translate

Levels of Learning Objectives (continued)

IV ANALYSIS	V SYNTHESIS	VI EVALUATION
Emphasis: Breaking into constituent parts and detecting relationships of the parts and the way they are organized and organizing material according to a coherent pattern	*Emphasis:* Putting together elements or parts to form a whole that reflects originality	*Emphasis:* On values, making qualitative or quantitative judgment, using criteria from internal or external sources and standards
analyze compare and contrast criticize debate deduce determine differentiate between (by analysis) draw conclusions formulate form generalizations make inferences organize relate (show relationships)	combine and organize design devise develop perform (in public) produce present (an original report or work) write (an original composition)	choose (based on evaluation) decide evaluate judge make a decision

This collection would not be possible without the cooperation of the following:

Science: Robert N. Hurst, Purdue University, Lafayette, Indiana; Kenneth H. Bush, David H. McGaw, and Curtis L. Smiley, West Lafayette High School, West Lafayette, Indiana; Joseph C. Gould, Charles J. Mott, and N. Gerald Langford, St. Petersburg Junior College, Clearwater, Florida; Miles H. Anderson, University of California, Los Angeles, California; Paul E. Trejo, De Anza College, Cupertino, California

Mathematics: Ephraim G. Salins, Montgomery College, Takoma Park, Maryland; Russell L. Fleury, University of Maryland, College Park, Maryland; Carl A. Grame and Daniel J. O'Donnell, De Anza College, Cupertino, California

Social Science: Wallace P. Harrison, Los Angeles Pierce College, Los Angeles, California; Robert A. Butler, Louisburg College, Louisburg, North Carolina; Richard L. Morgan, Mitchell College, Statesville, North Carolina; Dayton Y. Roberts, Texas Tech University, Lubbock, Texas; Alfred J. Furnweger, Santa Fe Community College, Gainesville, Florida; John E. Roueche, University of Texas, Austin, Texas; Barton R. Herrscher, College Associates, Austin, Texas; Rita and Stuart Johnson, School of Medicine, University of North Carolina, Chapel Hill, North Carolina; Marcia H. Perlstein, Opportunity II High School, San Francisco, California

Language Arts: Benson R. Schulman, Los Angeles Pierce College, Los Angeles, California; Lowell A. Draper, Modesto Community College, Modesto, California; Lucille M. Thomas, Grand Rapids Junior College, Grand Rapids, Michigan; Frances Coolidge, De Anza College, Cupertino, California; David J. Peterson, San Jose Unified School District, San Jose, California; Harold D. Sartain, Des Moines Area Community College, Ankeny, Iowa

Further acknowledgment is made to all who participated in developing objectives for Project PLAN* and *Behavioral Objectives: A Guide to Individualizing Learning.*

The Editors
Westinghouse Learning Press
Sunnyvale, California
15 September 1975

MATHEMATICS

Basic Math

02-005-005 **Perform the basic operations of addition and subtraction on whole numbers (integers), and solve related word problems. III**

Given any integer, recognize whether the integer is less than, equal to, or greater than another given integer. II

Identify the place value for each place (digit) of any integer. I

Find the sum of given numbers. II

Find the difference of two numbers. II

Demonstrate that numbers may be added in any order without changing the sum (order principle). III

Demonstrate that when three or more numbers are added, they may be grouped in any way without changing the sum (grouping principle). III

Solve word problems, using addition or subtraction of integers. III

Add and subtract signed whole numbers. II

Use the number line to demonstrate your understanding of addition. III

Solve word problems that involve addition or subtraction of signed numbers. III

02-005-010 **Perform the basic operations of multiplication and division on whole numbers (integers), and solve related word problems. III**

Identify: divisor, dividend, factors, product. I

Multiply two numbers, using the distributive property of multiplication over addition. II

Multiply any two whole numbers. II

Divide any integer by any other integer.   II

Solve division problems that involve 0.   III

Multiply or divide any integer by multiples of 10.   II

Multiply and divide signed numbers.   II

Solve word problems that involve multiplication and division of integers.   III

02-005-015   Explain and illustrate the properties of operations.   III

Illustrate the following: closure for addition, commutative principle for addition, associative principle for addition, identity element for addition.   III

Illustrate the following: closure for multiplication, commutative principle for multiplication, associative principle for multiplication, identity element for multiplication.   II

02-005-016   Perform basic operations of addition and subtraction on fractions, and solve related word problems.   III

Given any fraction, recognize whether the fraction is less than, greater than, or the same as another fraction.   II

Identify the numerator and denominator of a given fraction.   I

Express in numbers the proper fraction suggested by a diagram.   II

Draw a diagram, expressing a given fraction.   III

Given a proper fraction, express equivalent fractions.   II

Express a proper fraction in lowest terms.   II

Express an improper fraction as a whole number or as a mixed number.   II

Find the sum of two or more proper fractions with like denominators, and express the sum in lowest terms.   II

Find the sum of two or three mixed numbers with like denominators, and express the answer in lowest terms. II

Find the sum of fractions and mixed numbers with unlike denominators, and express the answer in lowest terms. II

Solve a word problem that requires addition of fractions, and express the answer in lowest terms. III

Given two proper fractions with like denominators, find the difference and the sum and express the answers in lowest terms. II

Subtract a fraction from a fraction when regrouping is not necessary, and write the difference in lowest terms. II

Subtract a fraction from a fraction when regrouping is necessary, and write the difference in lowest terms. II

Subtract a fraction or mixed number from a whole number, and write the answer in lowest terms. II

Given fractions and mixed numbers, or a mixed number and a fraction with unlike denominators, find the difference and express the answer in lowest terms. II

Solve word problems that require subtraction of fractions, and express the answers in lowest terms. III

Solve word problems that involve addition and subtraction of fractions, and express the answers in lowest terms. III

02-005-020 **Perform the basic operations of multiplication and division on fractions, and solve related word problems. III**

Multiply fractions or mixed fractions by a whole number and express the answer in lowest terms. II

Multiply a fraction by a fraction, a fraction by a mixed number, or a mixed fraction by a mixed number, and express the answer in lowest terms. II

Solve word problems, using multiplication of fractions.   III

Divide a whole number by a fraction or a mixed number. Divide a fraction or a mixed fraction by a whole number.   II

Divide a fraction by a fraction or a mixed fraction. Divide a mixed fraction by a mixed fraction.   II

Solve problems that involve the division of fractions, using the multiplicative inverse.   III

Solve word problems by using multiplication and division of fractions.   III

02-005-025   Perform the basic operation of addition and subtraction of decimals, and solve related word problems.   III

Recognize place value in decimals.   II

Express a given decimal to the nearest whole number, tenth, hundredth, or thousandth.   II

Express a decimal fraction as a mixed number, or as a common fraction with a denominator of 10, 100, or 1000.   II

Find the sum of given decimals.   II

Find the difference of two decimals.   II

Subtract any two given decimals.   II

Solve word problems that involve addition and/or subtraction of decimals.   III

Express a fraction or a mixed number as a decimal fraction.   II

02-005-030   Perform the basic operation of multiplication and division of decimals, and solve related word problems.   III

Multiply decimals when one of the factors is a whole number.   II

Multiply decimals when both factors are decimals. II

Divide a decimal by a whole number. II

Divide a decimal by a decimal. II

Divide a whole number by a decimal. II

Divide whole numbers when the divisor is a larger number than the dividend. II

Solve word problems that require division of decimals and by decimals. III

02-005-035 **Define ratio and proportion, and use this relationship to solve problems. III**

Express a ratio that shows a comparison of two quantities. II

Express a given ratio in several equivalent ratios. II

Use an equation to find the missing term in a proportion or to solve a problem that can be represented by a proportion. III

Use proportions to solve problems involving percents. III

Solve word problems that require the use of ratio and proportion. III

02-005-040 **Find the square root of a given number, and solve related word problems. III**

Define *square root.* I

Using a table of whole numbers and their squares, find the square or the square root of given numbers. II

Find by approximation the square root of any number. II

Solve word problems that involve square roots. III

02-005-045   Find squares and cubes of given numbers, and solve related word problems.   III

Define *square* and *cube*.   I

Using a table, find squares and cubes of numbers.   II

Multiply numbers to find their squares and cubes.   II

Solve word problems that involve squares and roots.   III

02-005-050   Using the four basic arithmetic operations, show that you can solve word problems by using integers, fractions, and decimals.   III

02-005-055   Estimate answers to problems.   III

Given a numeral less than 1,000,000, express the numeral to the nearest ten, hundred, or thousand.   II

Estimate the answers to problems by rounding the numerals involved to the nearest ten, hundred, or thousand.   III

Round off a given number to a given place.   II

Recognize significant numbers in any given numeral.   II

02-005-060   Use conventional measurements of time, space, and speed accurately, and devise a system for estimating measurements.   V

Relate appropriate terms of measurement to what is being measured.   IV

Compare two different systems of measurement.   IV

Given the appropriate tools of measurement, devise a means of measuring time.   V

Using parts of your body, devise a system of measuring length or height.   V

Given formulas and necessary measurements of figures, find perimeter, circumference, area, and volume.   II

02-005-065   **Convert from one system of measurement to another system.   III**

Using a table of liquid measures, express cups as pints, cups as quarts, quarts as gallons, pints as quarts, fluid ounces as cups, and fluid ounces as pints, and vice versa.   II

Using a table of weight measures, express ounces as pounds and pounds as tons, and vice versa.   II

Express linear measures of inches as feet, inches as yards, feet as yards, and feet as miles, and vice versa.   II

Convert liquid, linear, and weight measurements in the English system to the metric system, and vice versa.   III

Using a table of metric measures, express linear measures of millimeters as centimeters, centimeters as decimeters, decimeters as meters, centimeters as meters, and meters as kilometers, and vice versa.   II

Express time given on a 24-hour basis as time on a 12-hour basis, and vice versa.   II

Given a table of linear measures that includes kilometer, hectometer, decameter, meter, decimeter, centimeter, and millimeter, express a given measure as any of the other measures.   II

Given a table of metric units of mass (or weight), convert an amount in one unit to an amount in any of the other units.   III

Given a list of units in one measure, estimate the equal amount in another.   III

Given a list of measurement units, identify familiar items that approximate these measurements.   I

Use tables and formulas to convert one system of measurement to another.   III

02-005-070   **Perform arithmetic operations with measures of size, time, weight, distance, and capacity, and solve related word problems.   III**

Add or subtract measures of time (centuries, years, weeks, days, hours, minutes, seconds), expressing answers in simplest form.   II

Add or subtract measures of weight, expressing answers in simplest form.   II

Add or subtract liquid measures, expressing answers in simplest form.   III

Given rate of fuel consumption, solve problems that involve energy resources.   III

Given the measurements of an item, decrease or increase its measurements *n* times and derive its new measurements.   III

02-005-075   **Trace the development of number systems, and express symbols of one system in symbols of another system.   III**

Investigate at least one early number system, and express its symbols as equivalent arabic numbers (suggested systems: Egyptian, Babylonian, Mayan).   III

Express roman numerals as equivalent arabic numerals.   II

Express arabic numerals up to 5000 in roman numerals.   II

02-005-080   **Perform operations on bases other than base ten.   III**

Count in base two, base three, base four, base five, base six, base seven, base eight, and base nine ($base_2$, $base_3$, $base_4$, $base_5$, $base_6$, $base_7$, $base_8$, $base_9$).   II

Given a number in a base less than base ten, express the number as a base-ten number.   II

Given a base-ten number, express it as a number in a base less than base ten.   II

Express base-two numbers in expanded notation. II

Express base-two numbers in base ten and base-ten numbers in base two. II

Find the sum of numbers in base two. II

Find the difference of two numbers in base two. II

Find the product of numbers in base two. II

Find the quotient of numbers in base two. II

Solve problems with base-two numbers without converting the numbers to base-ten numbers. III

Express base-ten numbers in base-twelve numbers and base-twelve numbers in base-ten numbers. II

Add and subtract numbers in base twelve. II

Multiply and divide numbers in base twelve. II

Design a base system, complete with symbols, and solve problems by using the numbers of your base system. III

02-005-085 Express numbers in expanded and scientific notation. II

Write a given numeral in expanded form or, given a number in expanded form, write the numeral. II

Express any number in expanded notation. II

Express numbers in scientific notation. II

Using scientific notation, express the product of two numbers, each of which has more than 3 digits. II

Given a list of numbers expressed in scientific notation, select any not correctly expressed. II

02-005-090 Show your understanding of absolute value. II

Write the absolute value of a given number. II

Find the distance between points on a number line (subtraction with absolute value).   II

Find the sum of two given integers by following the rules stated in terms of absolute value.   II

Find the product of two given integers by following the rules stated in terms of absolute value.   II

Applied Math

02-010-005   **Given a word problem, apply a variety of techniques to help find the solution. III**

Draw a diagram for a given word problem. III

Given a word problem, list the extraneous information and/or list the information that is missing. I

Given a word problem, recognize the words that give clues to the appropriate operations to be used. II

Given a word phrase or sentence, convert it into a mathematical phrase or sentence or equation; or given a mathematical phrase, sentence, or equation, convert it into a word phrase or sentence. III

Given values for terms in a formula, solve the resulting equation. III

Select and use formulas for solving problems. III

Write an open sentence or equation for a given word problem (possibly containing extraneous information), and solve by using direct computation or by substitution (trial and error) or recognize the impossibility of finding a solution due to missing information. III

Estimate the answer for a given word problem, explaining how you arrived at the estimation. III

02-010-010   **Solve problems related to consumer purchases in cash transactions. III**

Given the price of one unit, find the price of n units. II

Given the price of n units, find the price of one unit. II

Given the cost of a specific quantity of a product and the cost of a different quantity of the same product, determine the cost per unit for both quantities to learn which rate is cheaper. III

Given a list of purchased items, the amount charged for each item, and the sales tax rate, demonstrate how a sales slip would show the price of each item, the tax, and the total bill.   III

Given the total bill and the amount of money paid to the cashier, determine the number and variety of bills and/or coins to be given in change.   III

Given the price of an article and the rate of sales tax, find the amount of tax and the total selling price.   II

Given the total price of an article and the amount of the tax, find the rate of sales tax.   II

Determine the rate of discount when the list price and the discount are known.   III

Determine the discount and the rate of discount when the list price and the net price are given.   III

02-010-015   **Solve problems related to consumer purchases that involve time payments, including interest and service charges, and make decisions regarding the total cost of such purchases.   VI**

Define the terms *charge account* and *revolving charge account,* and describe the advantages and disadvantages of each.   II

Given an unpaid balance on a revolving charge account with a 1% interest charge and the amount of the monthly payment, determine the total amount to be paid.   III

Given the price of an article, the amount of each monthly payment, and the total number of payments, determine the service charge and the rate of interest represented by the service charge.   III

Given the price of an article, the amount of each payment on an installment plan, and the number of payments on the installment plan, determine the total cost to buyers. Compare this cost with the cost of a bank loan for the same period of time at a given interest rate.   VI

02-010-020   **Solve problems related to saving and borrowing money, and make judgments based on your solutions.   VI**

Find the simple interest when the principal and the rate of interest are known.   II

Find the compound interest when the time, the principal, and the rate are given.   II

Given a number and an interest rate and using simple and compound interest tables, find the simple and compound interest.   II

Solve word problems involving simple and compound interest.   III

Given transactions that have taken place, prepare a savings-account passbook.   III

Given the annual interest rate, determine the interest on a specified amount of savings for a specified period of time.   III

Determine the amount of interest and the new balance for a savings account when a given amount of money is left in an account for a given period of time at a given rate of interest.   III

Given a bank's interest rate, a credit union's interest rate, and an amount of money to be borrowed, judge whether a loan from the bank or one from the credit union would be more advantageous to you.   VI

Given the beginning date of a loan and the length of time until the loan must be repaid, determine the date of maturity of the loan.   III

Given the amount of a loan, the rate of discount, and the length of time until the loan must be repaid, determine the bank discount and the proceeds.   III

02-010-025   **Perform procedures related to handling a checking account.   III**

Given the necessary information, prepare a deposit slip for a checking account.   III

Given transactions that have taken place, calculate the new balance for a checking account on the check stub or on a balance sheet. II

02-010-030 **Solve problems related to wages, salaries, and commissions and the related deductions. III**

Given the hourly wage and the number of hours worked in a week, determine the weekly, monthly, and annual wages. III

Given the time in and out, the company's regular work hours, overtime, and any sick leave and annual leave taken, prepare a time card for one week. III

Given a salary and rate of each deduction, determine the amount of take-home pay. III

Define and give an example of *income tax.* III

Given a weekly salary or wage and the number of exemptions, determine the income-tax deduction. III

Given the necessary information, complete a W-4 Withholding Exemption Form. II

Given an annual salary, the total tax deduction, and the number of exemptions, complete Form 1040-A. II

Given information on an imaginary income or using your own income, prepare all the necessary forms for completing an income tax report. III

Given a weekly salary or wage and the percent of deduction, find the amount of social security to be contributed by the employee. II

Explain and give an example of the following terms: *commission, net proceeds, sales, rate of commission.* II

Determine the amount of commission when the total sales and the rate based on total sales are known. III

Given the total sales and the amount of commission, determine the net proceeds. III

Given the total sales and the amount of commission, determine the rate of commission.   III

02-010-035   **Devise or develop a real or hypothetical family budget, basing expenditures on family size, needs, and desires. V**

Given an itemized list of expenditures and the annual income for a family, compute the percent of the income spent for each item.   II

Given the amount of annual income and the percent of the income to be spent on various items, compute the amount to be allocated to each item in a monthly budget.   II

02-010-040   **Solve problems related to the preparation and serving of food.   III**

Given a recipe, determine the amount of ingredients for two, four, and ten times as many.   III

Given a recipe that serves a stated number and the cost of each of the ingredients, determine the cost per serving.   III

Given a recipe and the number of calories in a specified amount of each of the ingredients, determine the number of calories per serving.   III

Given a chart of foods and calories for a specified amount, determine an individual's caloric intake based on actual varieties and amounts of food eaten.   III

02-010-045   **Solve problems related to decorating and remodeling, and make judgments based on your solutions.   VI**

Using a given scale, construct a scale drawing of a room, showing doors, windows, and a furniture arrangement of your choice.   III

Given the measurements of a room, the size and number of windows and doors, the amount of paint needed to cover a specified surface, and the cost of different kinds of paint, determine the cost of painting the room and decide which kind of paint will be most advantageous.   VI

Given the measurements of the windows in a room, a description of the kind of curtain desired, and the cost of different materials per yard, determine the cost of the material necessary for making the curtains and decide which material will be best for you.   VI

Given a scale drawing of an item to be constructed and the materials to be used, determine the amount of each material needed to build the item.   III

Given the measurements of an item, decrease or increase its measurements *n* times and determine its new measurements.   III

Given an itemized list of the amounts of various materials used in constructing an item and the cost per unit of each material, determine the total cost of the materials necessary to construct the item, and judge which material will be most appropriate.   VI

02-010-050   Solve problems related to consumption of utilities in a home.   III

Given a schedule of rates for electricity and an electric bill (from which the number of kilowatt-hours used can be determined), determine the total cost of the electricity used. Compare this cost with the amount shown on the electric bill.   III

Given a schedule of rates for gas and a gas bill (from which the number of cubic feet used can be determined), determine the total cost of the gas used and compare this cost with the amount shown on the gas bill.   III

Given a schedule of rates for water and a water bill (from which the number of cubic feet used can be derived), determine the total cost of the water used and compare this cost with the amount shown on the water bill. III

Given a table of telephone rates, the type and number of calls made in a given month, and the telephone bill for the month (including federal and local taxes), determine whether the total shown on the telephone bill is correct. III

02-010-055 **Apply mathematical operations to problems related to your education and career and use your solutions in making decisions. VI**

Given the number of people in an occupation and the total working population, find the percent of the total working population in the stated occupation. II

Given the present population and the expected rate of population increase, predict what the population will be in *n* years. III

Given the percent of people in a stated occupation and the predicted total working population in *n* years, predict the number of people in that occupation in *n* years. III

Given the average yearly wage for an occupation and the average years of employment in that occupation, find the average total life income for a person in that occupation. II

Given the cost of training and the total life income for an occupation, find what percent of life income the cost of training represents. II

Given an itemized list of college expenditures—including tuition, room and board, books, travel expenses, and personal expenses—for one month or year, compare the cost of attending a specified college for four years with the costs of spending two years at a community college and two years as a transfer. IV

Given the present average cost of attending college for one year and the predicted average rate of increase, predict the annual cost in *n* years.   III

Given the amount of a scholarship for one year and the total annual cost of college, find the percent of the total that is paid by the scholarship.   II

Given the total cost for one year of college, determine how much you would have to save yearly for any stated number of years to pay for one year of college, without considering the interest you might earn.   III

Investigate the comparative costs of a college education and a technical training program, and discuss (determine) the advantages of each.   IV

Investigate the comparative costs of a community college program and a four-year college program, and determine the advantages of each.   IV

02-010-060   Make judgments about your insurance needs based on comparative costs and benefits.   VI

Given a table of annual premiums for three types of life-insurance coverage (straight life, limited life, and endowment), the amount and type of insurance purchased, and the age of the policyholder at the time of purchase, determine what percent of the total amount of the policy will have been paid in premiums in *n* years.   III

Given a table of annual premiums for bodily injury, property damage, comprehensive damage, and collision insurance for different types of driving, determine the total annual premium for a car used for pleasure, for driving to work, or for business.   III

Given the annual premium rates of coverage for fire insurance and the amount of coverage, determine the premium for one year.   III

02-010-065   Solve problems related to property taxes.   III

Given the assessed value of the property, find the property tax when the rate is expressed in dollars per $100 or per $1000 of assessed valuation.   II

Given the assessed value of the property, find the property tax when the rate is expressed in mills or cents per $1.00 of assessed valuation or when the rate is expressed as a percent of the assessed valuation.   II

02-010-070   Make judgments related to selection of an automobile based on comparative costs.   VI

Given the original price of a car, its age, and its trade-in or resale value, determine the average annual depreciation of the car.   III

Given the original cost and the average annual depreciation of a car, determine the rate of depreciation.   III

Given the annual payments for taxes, insurance, gasoline, oil, repairs, interest, and depreciation, determine the total annual operating cost and the average monthly operating cost of a car.   III

Given the readings of the odometer on successive fillings of the gas tank and the amount of gasoline needed to fill the tank each time, determine the gas mileage for a given automobile.   III

Given any two of the following, determine the third: distance traveled, traveling time, average speed in miles per hour.   III

02-010-075   Plan a trip, using time, cost, and purpose as the basis for your plans.   III

Using a given map or chart, determine the distance between two specified cities.   III

Given the appropriate table of fares, compare the cost of traveling by plane, bus, ship, or train between any two cities.   III

Given the average speed and the average gas mileage for a car, the cost of gasoline, and the distance between two given cities, determine the traveling time and the cost of gasoline for a trip in this car between the two cities.   III

Given charts, convert money from one system to another and back and find the discount rates on the transactions.   II

02-010-080   Make judgments related to selecting modes of travel based on time, cost, and purpose.   VI

Using a plane, ship, bus, or train schedule, find the time it will take to travel between two cities on that mode of transportation.   II

From a map, determine road distances, air distances, and rail distances between given points.   III

02-010-085   Solve problems related to spectator and participant sports.   III

Given the number of field goals, the number of free throws made, and the time played by a basketball player, find the average scoring per minute played for that player.   II

Given the number of games and the total number of rebounds made by a basketball player, find the average number of rebounds per game for the player.   II

Given the number of games and the total number of assists made by a basketball player, find the average number of assists per game for the player.   II

Given the number of errors made by a baseball player and the number of chances he had to make an error, find the fielding percentage.   II

Given the wins and losses for two baseball teams, find how many games one team is behind the other.   II

Given the number of runs scored against a pitcher and the number of innings he pitched, find his earned-run average. II

Given the number of games won and the total number of games played for the baseball teams in a league, find the standing of a specific team. II

Given the number of hits made by a baseball player and his times at bat, find his batting average. II

Given the number of times at bat, and the types and number of hits made by a baseball player, find his slugging average. II

Given the total yards gained in rushing by a football team or player and the number of times the ball was carried, find the average number of yards gained in rushing. II

Given the number of yards gained by passing and the number of passes attempted in a football game, find the average number of yards gained by passing. II

Given the number of passes thrown and the number of passes completed by a football player in a number of games, find the average percent of passes completed (passing average). II

Given the number of games played by a football team and the number of points for each game, find the average number of points made per game by the team. II

02-010-090 Plan the redecoration of a room for a customer, considering the customer's budget, needs, and desires. III

Make a drawing of a room to a given scale, showing doors, windows, and a furniture arrangement of your choice. III

Given the measurements of a room, the size and number of windows and doors, the amount of paint needed to cover a given surface, and the cost of the paint, find the cost of painting the room. II

Given the measurements of the windows in a room, a description of the kind of curtain desired, and the cost of material, hardware, and installation, find the cost of the completed curtains.   II

02-010-095   Solve problems related to the handling of money through banks and other lending institutions as related to deposits, checking accounts, and loans.   III

Given the beginning date of a loan and the length of time until the loan must be repaid, compute the date of maturity of the loan.   II

Given the amount of a loan, the rate of discount, and the length of time until the loan must be repaid, compute the bank discount and the proceeds.   II

Define *simple interest, compound interest,* and *interest figured on unpaid balance.*   I

Compute simple interest when the principal, the rate of interest, and the time are known.   II

Compute compound interest when the time, principal, and rate are given.   II

Given a principal, an interest rate, and the time, use simple and compound interest tables to compute simple and compound interest.   II

Given the necessary information, complete a deposit slip for a checking account.   II

Given transactions that have taken place, compute the new balance for a checking account on the check stub or on a balance sheet.   II

Use a hand calculator to compute interest at a given rate on a given principal when it is compounded daily, monthly, and quarterly.   III

02-010-100   **Analyze costs and prices, and use this information in determining profit margin.   IV**

Explain and give an example of the following terms: *profit, loss, margin, overhead, selling price, cost.*   II

Given the cost of an article and its selling price, determine the margin.   III

Given the cost of an article, the selling price, and the overhead, determine the profit or the loss.   III

Given the cost of an article and the profit, find the percent of profit on the cost.   II

Given the cost and the percent of margin on the cost, determine the margin and the selling price.   III

Given a list of purchased items, the amount charged for each item, and the sales tax rate, prepare a sales slip that shows the price of each item, the tax, and the total bill.   III

02-010-105   **Analyze costs and prices, considering discounts and commissions, and use this information to determine profit margin.   IV**

Given the price of one unit, find the price of any number of units.   II

Given the price of *n* units, find the price of one unit.   II

Given the cost of a specific quantity of a product and the cost of a different quantity of the same product, calculate the costs per unit for both quantities to determine which rate is cheaper.   II

Explain and give examples of the following terms: *marked price (list price), discount, net price.*   II

Compute the net price when the list price and the discount rate are given.   II

Compute the discount when the list price and the discount rate are given.   II

Compute the rate of discount when the list price and the discount are given. III

Compute the discount and the rate of discount when the list price and the net price are given. III

Explain and give examples of each of the following terms: *commission, net proceeds, sales, rate of commission.* I

Given the total sales and the amount of commission, compute the net proceeds. II

Given the total sales and the amount of commission, compute the rate of commission. II

Compute the amount of commission when the total sales and the rate based on total sales are known. II

02-010-110 Solve problems related to construction of buildings and furnishings. III

Given a scale drawing of an item to be constructed and the materials to be used, find the amount of each material needed to build it. II

Given an itemized list of the amounts of various materials used in constructing an item and the cost per unit of each material, find the total cost of the materials necessary to construct the item. II

02-010-115 Solve problems related to insurance needs in business. III

Given a table of annual premiums for three types of life insurance coverage (straight life, limited life, and endowment), the amount and type of insurance purchased, and the age of the policyholder at the time of purchase, find what percent of the total amount of the policy will have been paid in premiums in a given number of years. II

Given a table of annual premiums for bodily injury, property damage, comprehensive damage, and collision insurance for different types of driving, compute the total annual premium for a car used for pleasure, for driving to work, or for business. II

Given the annual premium rates of coverage for fire insurance and the amount of coverage, compute the premium for one year. II

02-010-120   Solve problems related to wages and salaries. III

Given the number of workers, hourly wages, and the number of hours worked per week, find the weekly, monthly, and annual cost of labor for a business. II

Given the times in and out, the company's regular work hours, the overtime, and any sick leave and annual leave taken, prepare a time card for one week and compute the wages and deductions. III

02-010-125   Analyze business costs related to the building occupied. IV

Given a schedule of rates for gas and a gas bill (from which the number of cubic feet used can be determined), find the total cost of the gas used and compare this cost with the amount shown on the gas bill. II

Given a schedule of rates for electricity and an electric bill (from which the number of kilowatt-hours used can be determined), find the total cost of the electricity used and compare this cost with the amount shown on the electric bill. II

Given a schedule of rates for water and a water bill (from which the number of cubic feet used can be determined), find the total cost of the water used and compare this cost with the amount shown on the water bill. II

Given a table of telephone rates, the type and number of calls made in a given month, and the telephone bill for the month, calculate the total cost of the telephone service for the month (including federal and local taxes) and compare this amount with the total shown on the telephone bill. IV

Given prices per square foot and dimensions for each of the following—offices, shop area, and storage—compute and compare costs for rental of two different buildings. IV

02-010-130   Use rate charts and other given information to make decisions regarding shipping and mailing that are based on time and cost.   VI

Given the restrictions on size and weight of letters and packages, determine whether or not a given letter or package can be mailed and state the reason.   III

Given a table of parcel-post rates and information about the distance between cities, find the cost of mailing a given package from one city to any other city in the United States.   II

Given a table of rates for first-class mail, air mail, special delivery, and registered mail, find the cost of mailing a specific letter or package first class, air mail, special delivery, or registered.   II

Given a table of rates for freight, express, parcel-delivery service, bus, and air express, find the cost and time for shipping a specific package.   II

02-010-135   Analyze the budget of a given business and recommend possible changes based on income and needs.   IV

Given an itemized list of expenditures and the annual income for a business, find the percent of income spent for each item.   II

Given the amount of annual income and the percent of income to be spent on various items, calculate the amount to be allocated to each item in a monthly budget.   II

Analyze equipment costs and depreciation, and make recommendations based on your analysis.   IV

Given the original price of an item of equipment, its age, and its trade-in or resale value, find the average annual depreciation of the item.   II

Given the original cost and the average annual depreciation of a piece of equipment, find the rate of depreciation.   II

Given the annual payments for taxes, insurance, gasoline, oil, repairs, interest, and depreciation, find the total annual operating cost and the average monthly operating cost of a piece of equipment. II

02-010-140 **Identify key terms related to the operation of computers, and describe their basic functions. II**

Describe the meaning of the shapes of boxes in a flow-chart. II

Given a flowchart depicting the steps for solving a program (an algorithm), find the output value(s) that the program computes for a specified set of input values. II

Draw a flowchart of the algorithm that would be used to solve a given problem in computation. II

02-010-145 **Use a slide rule to carry out basic operations and to find squares and square roots. III**

Given a slide rule, identify the following parts and their functions: the rule proper, the slide, the runner, and the scales. I

Using the slide rule, multiply numbers. II

Using the slide rule, divide a number by another number. II

Using the slide rule, square any number. III

Using the slide rule, find the square root of any number. III

02-010-150 **Use a simple hand calculator to solve problems related to business, career, and consumer problems. III**

Perform all basic operations on a given type of electronic calculator. II

Recognize the difference between algebraic and arithmetic logic in a given hand calculator and the differences involved in entering numbers and functions. II

Recognize the following features in a given calculator: memory function, floating decimal, fixed point, decimal, overflow, rounding off, truncation. II

Use the features of a given calculator to solve word problems involving basic operations on whole numbers, fractions, and decimals. III

Geometry

02-015-005 **Describe and classify geometric figures by using their properties. II**

Identify all regular polygons that have from three to ten sides. I

Find and describe the vertices and the diagonals of a given polygon. II

Recognize the figure formed by joining the midpoints of the four sides of a given quadrilateral. II

Identify the following parts of a circle: center, radius, diameter, chord. I

Define *acute triangle, right triangle, obtuse triangle, isosceles triangle, scalene triangle,* and *equilateral triangle,* and recognize examples of each. II

Recognize given geometric figures as congruent or non-congruent. II

Classify given polygons as convex or concave by examining their diagonals. II

Find measurements indirectly by using corresponding sides of similar triangles. II

02-015-010 **Find perimeters, areas, and volumes of geometric figures. II**

Given the measure of each side of a polygon, find its perimeter. II

Given the measure of the circumference, the radius, or the diameter of a circle, find the other two dimensions. II

Given the measures of the sides of a polygon, find its area. II

Given the measures of the base and height of a triangle, find its area. II

Given the measures of the base and altitude of a parallelogram, find its area. II

Given the formula for finding the area of a trapezoid and the measures of the bases and height of a trapezoid, find its area. II

Given the formula for finding the area of a circle and the measure of the radius or of the diameter of a circle, find its area. II

Given the length of one edge of a cube, find the volume. II

Given the dimensions of a rectangular prism, find its volume. II

Given the measures of the height and the radius of the base of a cylinder, find the volume. II

02-015-015   **Using formulas, solve word problems that require finding the perimeters, areas, and volumes of geometric shapes. III**

Using formulas, find the perimeters of triangles, squares, rectangles, parallelograms, trapezoids, other polygons, and circles. II

Using formulas, find the areas of rectangles, squares, parallelograms, triangles, trapezoids, and circles. II

Using formulas, find the volumes of rectangular solids, cylinders, pyramids, cones, and spheres. II

Given a word problem that involves a geometric shape, draw the figure and label the dimensions given in the problem. III

02-015-020   **Construct and measure geometric figures. III**

Using a protractor, measure to the nearest degree any given angle from 0° to 180°. II

Using a protractor, draw right angles, straight angles, acute angles, and obtuse angles of specified degrees, accurate to the nearest degree. III

Using a protractor and a straightedge, draw and measure angles that are correct to within two degrees. III

Using a compass and/or a straightedge, determine whether two line segments are congruent, whether two angles are congruent, and whether two triangles are congruent. III

Using a compass and a straightedge, construct the bisector of a given line segment. III

Use a protractor and a straightedge to construct acute, right, obtuse, straight, or reflex angles and draw adjacent, vertical, complementary, or supplementary angle pairs of specified sizes. III

Use a compass and an unmarked straightedge to construct a duplicate of a given angle of less than 360° and to construct the bisector of a given angle of less than 360°. III

Use a compass and an unmarked straightedge to construct a line parallel to a given line through a given point not on the line. III

Use a compass and an unmarked straightedge to construct the perpendicular to a line segment at a given point on the line segment and to construct the perpendicular bisector of a line segment. III

Use a compass and an unmarked straightedge to construct the perpendicular to a line segment from a given point not on the line segment. III

Use a compass and an unmarked straightedge to divide a line segment into a specified number of parts of equal length. III

Use a compass and an unmarked straightedge to construct a square, given the length of each side, and to construct the duplicate of a given quadrilateral. III

Use a compass and an unmarked straightedge to construct a circle, given the length of the radius, and to construct a circle through three given points (not all on the same line).   III

Use a compass and an unmarked straightedge to construct the tangent to a circle at a given point on the circle.   III

Using a compass to duplicate the angles, demonstrate that each of the following is true for a given case.   III
1. The sum of the measures of the angles of any triangle is 180°.
2. The sum of the measures of the angles of any parallelogram is 360°.
3. If two parallel lines are cut by a transversal, the sum of the measures of two interior angles on the same side of the transversal is 180°.

Using the statement "If two lines are cut by a transversal so that the sum of two interior angles on the same side of the transversal is 180°, then the lines are parallel" and using a compass to duplicate angles and to compare lengths of line segments, demonstrate that each of the following is true for a given case.   III
1. The line segment joining the midpoints of two sides of a triangle is parallel to the third side and measures half its length.
2. The line segments joining the consecutive midpoints of the sides of any quadrilateral form a parallelogram.

Solve word problems that involve the measurement, construction, and addition of angles.   III

Define and construct the angle bisectors, medians, and altitudes of a triangle.   III

Given three sides, construct a triangle. Given two sides and the included angle, construct a triangle. Given two angles and the included side, construct a triangle.   III

Construct a perpendicular to a line through a point on the line, through the midpoint of the line, and through a point not on the line.   III

Construct a line parallel to a given line through a given point, and divide a given line segment into any number of congruent parts. III

Given an arc of a circle, construct the bisector of the arc and find the center of the circle. III

Construct an inscribed circle within a given triangle. III

02-015-025 Demonstrate and apply the Pythagorean relationship. III

Using the Pythagorean relationship, recognize right triangles. II

Using inductive reasoning (experimental method), derive the Pythagorean relationship ($a^2 + b^2 = c^2$). III

Using the Pythagorean relationship, find the length of the hypotenuse of a right triangle when the lengths of the legs are given. II

Using the Pythagorean relationship, find the length of one of the legs of a given right triangle when the lengths of the hypotenuse and the other leg are given. II

Solve word problems that require use of the Pythagorean relationship. III

Given the lengths of two sides of a right triangle, find the length of the third side. II

02-015-030 Apply the Pythagorean theorem, the concept of similar triangles, or trigonometric ratios to make indirect measurements. III

Use proportions to find unknown lengths of sides in similar triangles. II

Solve word problems that involve indirect measurement by using similar triangles or the Pythagorean theorem. III

Apply the concept of similar triangles or the Pythagorean theorem to make indirect measurements of distances outside the classroom.   III

Express the sine, the cosine, or the tangent ratio for the two acute angles of a right triangle.   II

Using a table, find the value of the sine, of the cosine, or of the tangent for a given acute angle.   II

Using a table, find the angle that corresponds to the given value of a sine, of a cosine, or of a tangent.   II

Given the measures of one acute angle and of one side in a right triangle, use a trigonometric ratio of either acute angle to find the length of another side.   II

Given the measures of two sides of a right triangle, use a trigonometric ratio to find the measure of one of the acute angles.   II

Solve word problems that involve indirect measurement by using trigonometric ratios.   III

Apply the concept of trigonometric ratios to make indirect measurements of distances and angles outside the classroom.   III

02-015-035   Apply definitions and properties of angles and triangles to the solution of problems.   III

Recognize the interior, exterior, and vertices of angles and of triangles, and recognize different types of triangles.   II

Solve word problems that involve the measurement, construction, and addition of angles.   III

Apply definitions of *linear pair, supplementary, complementary, right angle, vertical angle,* and *adjacent angle* to prove congruence of angle theorems.   III

Apply the basic congruence, or side-angle-side (SAS) postulate, in formal proofs.   III

Apply the angle-side-angle (ASA) theorem in formal proofs. III

Using SAS and/or ASA, prove that two sides of a triangle are congruent if and only if the angles opposite these sides are congruent (isosceles-triangle theorem). III

Apply the side–side–side (SSS) theorem in formal proofs. III

Apply the theorem that an exterior angle of a triangle is greater than either remote interior angle to prove theorems and to solve problems. III

Prove and apply the side–angle–angle theorem (SAA) and the congruence theorems for right triangles (hypotenuse–angle, hypotenuse–leg, and leg–leg). III

Prove theorems and solve word problems by using the theorem of inequality of sides and angles within a triangle. III

Use the triangle inequality theorem (sides) to solve related word problems and to write proofs. III

Apply the following theorem to problem situations: "If two sides of one triangle are ≅ respectively to two sides of a second Δ and the included angle of the first Δ is larger than the included angle of the second Δ, then the third side of the first triangle is larger than the third side of the second." III

State and apply the Pythagorean theorem in proofs and problem situations. III

Solve word problems that require a discrimination between the definitions of *proportion, ratio, geometric mean* (mean proportion), and *similarity* (~). III

Given the fact that a line intersects two sides of a triangle and is parallel to the third side, prove theorems that are direct consequences of this fact and apply the theorems in solving problems. III

Solve word problems and write proofs using the theorem that if three angles of one triangle are congruent to three angles of a second triangle, then the triangles are similar.   III

Given the following two theorems, prove theorems that are dependent on these two and apply them in solving problems.   III
1. Two triangles are similar if two sides of one are proportional to two corresponding sides of the other and if the included angles are congruent.
2. Two triangles are similar if the three sides of one are proportional to the three sides of the other.

Solve word problems and write proofs applying theorems dealing with similarities between right triangles.   III

Find the ratio of the areas of similar triangles, given the dimensions of any corresponding parts.   II

02-015-040   Apply definitions and properties of lines and planes to the solution of problems.   III

Recognize definitions of the following words: *intersection, union, collinear, coplanar.*   II

Using absolute value, find the distance between any two points on a line.   II

Identify conditions that determine a line. (Line postulate: For every two points there is exactly one line that contains both points.)   I

Identify symbols and definitions for *line, segment, ray, opposite rays, midpoint, endpoint, length, angle, triangle,* and *space.*   I

Apply the definition of *congruence* ($\cong$) to line segments, angles, and polygons to solve problems.   III

Identify all conditions that determine a plane.   I

Describe the separation of a line by a point, a plane by a line, and a space by a plane in terms of convex sets.   II

In solving problems and in writing proofs, apply the theorem that in a given plane, through a given point of a given line or through a given external point, there is one and only one line (plane) perpendicular ($\perp$) to a given line.   III

Prove and apply the theorem that the perpendicular bisector of a segment in a plane is the set of all points of that plane that are equidistant from the endpoints of the segment.   III

In solving problems and in writing proofs, apply the theorem that if a line is perpendicular to each of two intersecting lines at their point of intersection, then it is perpendicular to the plane that contains them.   III

Prove that the shortest segment to a plane from an external point is the perpendicular segment between them. (Use indirect proof.)   III

Define and recognize parallel lines, skew lines, transversal, alternate interior angles, and corresponding angles.   II

Apply the relationships between parallel lines and a transversal in writing proofs.   III

Prove that the sum of the measures of the angles in a triangle is 180°, and apply related theorems in solving problems.   III

Use the relationship of the sides in a 30–60–90 triangle to solve word problems and to write proofs.   III

In writing proofs, apply the theorem that if three or more parallel lines intercept congruent segments on one transversal, then they intercept congruent segments on any transversal.   III

Prove the following theorem and answer related questions: "If two parallel planes are intersected by another plane, the lines of intersection are parallel."   III

Apply the properties of parallelism and perpendicularity of lines and planes in solving problems and in writing proofs.   III

After defining the term *projection,* solve word problems related to finding the projection of a set of points.   III

Using the statement "If two lines are cut by a transversal so that the sum of two interior angles on the same side of the transversal is 180°, then the lines are parallel" and using a compass to duplicate angles and to compare lengths of line segments, demonstrate that each of the following is true for a given case.   III
1. The line segment joining the midpoints of two sides of a triangle is parallel to the third side and measures half its length.
2. The line segments joining the consecutive midpoints of the sides of any quadrilateral form a parallelogram.

02-015-045   Apply definitions and properties of quadrilaterals and other polygons to the solution of problems.   III

Recognize and define the following terms: *quadrilateral, convex quadrilateral, consecutive angles, opposite angles, diagonal, vertices, base, altitude, trapezoid, parallelogram, rectangle, square, rhombus.*   II

Prove and apply theorems concerning diagonals, opposite sides, opposite angles, and consecutive angles of parallelograms.   III

Prove and apply theorems concerning diagonals, opposite sides, and opposite angles of quadrilaterals (sufficient conditions for a parallelogram).   III

Prove and apply theorems dealing with the angles and diagonals of a rhombus, a rectangle, and a square.   III

Prove and apply the theorem concerning the relationship between the segment that connects the midpoints of two sides of a triangle and the third side.   III

Apply the area, congruence, area addition, and unit (square) postulates for polygons in solving problems.   III

Prove and apply theorems concerning the areas of rectangles and triangles in writing proofs and solving problems.   III

Prove and apply theorems concerning the areas of trapezoids and parallelograms in writing related proofs and solving problems. III

Define the following terms as they apply to polygons: *vertices, sides, angles, diagonals, perimeter, apothem.* Name given polygons and classify them as regular or irregular, convex or not convex. II

Find the number of diagonals in a polygon of *n* sides by using the formula $D = \frac{n}{2}(n - 3)$, and find the sum of the measures of the angles of a polygon of *n* sides by using the formula $S_n = (n - 2)180$. II

02-015-050 **Apply definitions and properties of circles to the solution of problems. III**

Define and solve problems concerning the common properties of circles and spheres in relation to center, radius, diameter, great circle, chord, secant, tangent, interior, and exterior. III

Prove the theorem that a line tangent to a circle (sphere) is perpendicular to the radius at the point of contact. Apply this fact in solving problems and writing proofs. III

Prove that if a diameter is perpendicular to a chord, it bisects the chord. Apply this theorem to solve related problems and write proofs. III

Prove that congruent chords in the same circle or in congruent circles are equidistant from the center of the circle (sphere) and apply this theorem in solving problems and writing related proofs. III

Use the definitions of *central angle, major arc, minor arc, semicircle, degree measure, arc addition, angular degree,* and *degree of arc* to solve related problems. III

Prove theorems and apply them in solving problems that concern the relationship between central angles and intercepted arcs. III

Prove that the measure of an inscribed angle is half the measure of its intercepted arc, and apply this theorem in writing proofs and solving problems.   III

Prove theorems concerning the angles formed by tangents, secants, and chords, and apply them to related problems and proofs.   III

Prove theorems related to the lengths of segments formed by secants and tangents, and apply them to related problems and proofs.   III

Use the circumference formula, $C = 2\pi r$, the area formula, $A = \pi r^2$, and the number π to find the circumference and the area of any circle.   II

Using the formulas for the circumference and area of a circle, derive the formula for the area of a sector $\left(\dfrac{x}{360}\pi r^2\right.$, where x is the number of degrees in the sector) and use this formula to solve problems.   III

02-015-055   Construct deductive and indirect proofs and proofs that use coordinate geometry.   III

Given arguments illustrating inductive and deductive reasoning, classify each as inductive or deductive.   II

Recognize definitions of the following words: *theorem, definition, postulate, axiom, assumption, proof, direct proof, indirect proof.*   II

Apply the definitions of *linear pair, supplementary, complementary, right angle, vertical angle,* and *adjacent angle* to prove congruence-of-angle theorems.   III

Apply the basic congruence, or side–angle–side (SAS) postulate, in formal proofs.   III

Apply the angle–side–angle (ASA) theorem in formal proofs.   III

Using SAS and/or ASA, prove that two sides of a triangle are congruent if and only if the angles opposite these sides are congruent (isosceles-triangle theorem).   III

Apply the theorem that an exterior angle of a triangle is greater than either remote interior angle to prove theorems and solve problems. III

Prove and apply the side–angle–angle (SAA) theorem and the congruence theorems for right triangles (hypotenuse–angle, hypotenuse–leg, leg–leg). III

Prove theorems and solve word problems by using the theorem of inequality of sides and angles within a triangle. III

Use the triangle-inequality theorem (sides) to solve related word problems and to write proofs. III

In solving problems and writing proofs, apply the theorem that in a given plane, through a given point of a given line or through a given external point, there is one and only one line (plane) perpendicular ($\perp$) to a given line. III

Prove and apply the theorem that the perpendicular bisector of a segment in a plane is the set of all points of that plane that are equidistant from the endpoints of the segment. III

In solving problems and writing proofs, apply the theorem that if a line is perpendicular to each of two intersecting lines at their point of intersection, then it is perpendicular to the plane that contains them. III

Prove that the shortest segment to a plane from an external point is the perpendicular segment between them. (Use indirect proof.) III

In writing proofs, apply the relationships between parallel lines and a transversal. III

Prove that the sum of the measures of the angles in a triangle is 180°, and apply related theorems to solve problems. III

Use the relationship of the sides in a 30–60–90 triangle to solve word problems and write proofs. III

In writing proofs, apply the theorem that if three or more parallel lines intercept congruent segments on one transversal, then they intercept congruent segments on any transversal.   III

Prove and apply theorems concerning diagonals, opposite sides, opposite angles, and consecutive angles of parallelograms.   III

Prove and apply theorems concerning diagonals, opposite sides, and opposite angles of quadrilaterals (sufficient conditions for a parallelogram).   III

Prove and apply theorems dealing with the angles and diagonals of a rhombus, a rectangle, and a square.   III

Prove and apply the theorem concerning the relationship between the segment that connects the midpoints of two sides of a triangle and the third side.   III

Prove the following theorem and answer related questions: "If two parallel planes are intersected by another plane, the lines of intersection are parallel."   III

Apply the properties of parallelism and perpendicularity of lines and planes to solving problems and writing proofs.   III

Prove and apply theorems concerning the areas of rectangles and triangles in writing proofs and in solving problems.   III

Prove and apply theorems concerning the areas of trapezoids and parallelograms to write related proofs and to solve problems.   III

Given the fact that a line intersects two sides of a triangle and is parallel to the third side, prove theorems that are direct consequences of this fact and apply the theorems in solving problems.   III

Solve word problems and write proofs by using the theorem that if three angles of one triangle are congruent to three angles of a second triangle, then the triangles are similar.   III

Given the following two theorems, prove theorems that are dependent on these two and apply them in solving problems. III

1. Two triangles are similar if two sides of one are proportional to two corresponding sides of the other and if the included angles are congruent.
2. Two triangles are similar if the three sides of one are proportional to the three sides of the other.

Solve word problems and write proofs by applying theorems that deal with similarity between right triangles. III

Prove the theorem that a line tangent to a circle (sphere) is perpendicular to the radius at the point of contact, and apply this fact in solving problems and in writing proofs. III

Prove that if a diameter is perpendicular to a chord, it bisects the chord. Apply this theorem to solve related problems and to write proofs. III

Prove that congruent chords in the same circle or in congruent circles are equidistant from the center of the circle (sphere), and apply this theorem in solving related problems and in writing related proofs. III

Prove theorems and apply them in solving problems concerning the relationship between central angles and intercepted arcs. III

Prove that the measure of an inscribed angle is half the measure of its intercepted arc, and apply this theorem in writing proofs and in solving problems. III

Prove theorems concerning the angles formed by tangents, secants, and chords, and apply them in solving related problems and in writing proofs. III

Prove theorems related to the lengths of segments formed by secants and tangents, and apply them to related problems and proofs. III

Given a theorem to prove by coordinate geometry methods, apply the most appropriate coordinates to make the algebraic calculations as easy as possible. III

Given a theorem to prove by coordinate geometry methods, apply the most appropriate coordinates to ensure that the proof is a general case, not a special case. III

Given a geometry theorem, prove the theorem by applying coordinate geometry definitions, theorems, and techniques. III

02-015-060 Apply knowledge and techniques of coordinate geometry of the line in solving problems. III

Plot or recognize ordered pairs and triples on a Cartesian coordinate system. II

When given two points contained in a line, use the definition of the *slope of a line* to find the slope. II

Apply the following theorem in solving problems: "Two nonvertical lines are parallel if and only if they have the same slope." III

Apply the following theorem in solving problems: "Two nonvertical lines are perpendicular if and only if the product of their slopes is equal to -1." III

Prove and apply to problems the following distance formula: $dP_1P_2 = \sqrt{(x_2 - x_1)^2 + (y_2 - y_1)^2}$ III

Prove and apply to problems the following midpoint formula: "If (x,y) is the midpoint of the segment with endpoints (x_1, y_1) and (x_2, y_2), then $x = \dfrac{x_1 + x_2}{2}$ and $y = \dfrac{y_1 + y_2}{2}$." III

Apply the following theorem in solving problems: "If P is a point between P_1 and P_2 and $\dfrac{dPP_1}{dPP_2} = r$, then the coordinates of P are $\left(\dfrac{x_1 + rx_2}{1 + r}, \dfrac{y_1 + ry_2}{1 + r}\right)$. The coordinates of P_1 are (x_1, y_1), and the coordinates of P_2 are (x_2, y_2)." III

Determine sets of points that satisfy any of the following and graph them: ||, =, <, >, or combinations thereof. III

Describe a line by writing an equation that is in the point-slope form. II

Given the equation of a line in the point-slope form, graph the line. III

Describe a line by writing an equation that is in the slope-intercept form. II

Given the equation of a line in slope-intercept form, graph the equation. III

Given a theorem to prove by coordinate-geometry methods, apply the most appropriate coordinates to make the algebraic calculations as easy as possible. III

Given a theorem to prove by coordinate-geometry methods, apply the most appropriate coordinates to ensure that the proof is a general case, not a special case. III

Given a geometry theorem, prove the theorem by applying coordinate-geometry definitions, theorems, and techniques. III

Trigonometry

02-020-005 **Apply the definitions, relationships, and theorems of numerical trigonometry to the solution of problems. III**

On the coordinate plane, recognize angles in standard position and solve related problems. II

Define *sine, cosine,* and *tangent.* I

Solve word problems that involve indirect measurement by using trigonometric ratios. III

Make indirect measurements of distances and of angles by using trigonometric ratios. III

From sets of ordered pairs of real numbers or from linear functions that determine the terminal side of an angle θ, find the value of the sine of θ (sin θ) and of the cosine of θ (cos θ). II

Define the tangent, cotangent, secant, and cosecant functions. Given one of the trigonometric ratios for any angle θ, find the values of the remaining trigonometric functions. II

Find the values of the functions of quadrantal angles and the special angles (30°, 45°, 60°). II

Apply the values of the functions of quadrantal angles and the special angles (30°, 45° 60°) to relate trigonometric functions to their cofunctions. III

Determine reference angles for any angle θ in standard position, and solve corresponding function value problems. III

Use a table of values of trigonometric functions to find the value of trigonometric functions and angles from a given numerical value of a trigonometric function of some angle. III

Use logarithms of the values of trigonometric functions to solve problems that involve operations with trigonometric functions. III

Solve word problems that require construction of right triangles and computations with trigonometric functions. III

Use the distance formula to derive the Law of Cosines ($c^2 = a^2 + b^2 - 2ab$, cos C), and apply the Law of Cosines in solving problems. III

Given two sides and the included angle of a triangle, derive the formula for its area. III

Given two sides and the included angle of a triangle, find the area of a triangle. II

Derive the Law of Sines, $\dfrac{\sin A}{a} = \dfrac{\sin B}{b} = \dfrac{\sin C}{c}$, and use this law to solve related problems. III

Given the measurements of two sides and one angle (not the included angle) of a triangle, find all the triangles that have those measurements. II

Given the measurements of some of the sides and/or angles of a triangle, find the measurements of the remaining sides and/or angles. II

Solve word problems that require the use of trigonometric functions. Construct meaningful diagrams as an aid in solving these problems. III

02-020-010 **Derive and use the multiple-angle formulas to prove that an equation is an identity and to solve an equation. III**

Prove that a given equation is a trigonometric identity by use of the reciprocal, quotient, and Pythagorean relation. III

Given two points (P and Q) in a plane, with p and q being the distance from the origin to those points with respective position angles α and β, and using $x = p \cos \theta$ and $y = p \sin \theta$ and the rectangular coordinate distance formula, derive the distance formula $(PQ)^2 = p^2 + q^2 - 2pq (\cos \alpha \cos \beta + \sin \alpha \sin \beta)$. Use the distance formula to solve problems. III

Derive the formula for the cosine of the difference of two angles and solve related problems.   III

Given $\cos (\alpha - \beta) = \cos \alpha \cos \beta + \sin \alpha \sin \beta$, derive the following formulas.   III
1. $\cos (\alpha + \beta) = \cos \alpha \cos \beta - \sin \alpha \sin \beta$
2. $\sin (\alpha + \beta) = \sin \alpha \cos \beta + \cos \alpha \sin \beta$
3. $\sin (\alpha - \beta) = \sin \alpha \cos \beta - \cos \alpha \sin \beta$
4. $\tan (\alpha + \beta) = \dfrac{\tan \alpha + \tan \beta}{1 - \tan \alpha \tan \beta}$
5. $\tan (\alpha - \beta) = \dfrac{\tan \alpha - \tan \beta}{1 + \tan \alpha \tan \beta}$

From the sum and difference formulas, derive and use the double and half-angle formulas.   III

1. $\sin 2B = 2 \sin B \cos B$

2. $\cos 2B = \cos^2 B - \sin^2 B$

3. $\tan 2B = \dfrac{2 \tan B}{1 - \tan^2 B}$

4. $\sin \dfrac{\theta}{2} = \sqrt{\dfrac{1 - \cos \theta}{2}}$

5. $\cos \dfrac{\theta}{2} = \sqrt{\dfrac{1 + \cos \theta}{2}}$

6. $\tan \dfrac{\theta}{2} = \dfrac{1 - \cos \theta}{1 + \cos \theta}$

From the sum and difference formulas, derive and use the sum and product formulas.   III
1. $2 \sin \alpha \cos \beta = \sin (\alpha + \beta) + \sin (\alpha - \beta)$
2. $2 \cos \alpha \cos \beta = \cos (\alpha + \beta) + \cos (\alpha - \beta)$
3. $-2 \sin \alpha \sin \beta = \cos (\alpha + \beta) - \cos (\alpha - \beta)$
4. $\sin A + \sin B = 2 \sin \dfrac{A + B}{2} \cos \dfrac{A - B}{2}$
5. $\sin A - \sin B = 2 \cos \dfrac{A + B}{2} \sin \dfrac{A - B}{2}$
6. $\cos A + \cos B = 2 \cos \dfrac{A + B}{2} \cos \dfrac{A - B}{2}$
7. $\cos A - \cos B = -2 \sin \dfrac{A + B}{2} \sin \dfrac{A - B}{2}$

Solve open sentences that may require a substitution of any of the trigonometric identities.   III

02-020-015   Use the definitions of the circular functions and their inverses to graph and to solve analytic problems.   III

Convert degree measurements to radian measurements, or vice versa, and solve related problems.   III

Define the circular functions, and solve related problems. III

Graph on the real number plane the functions $y = \sin x$, $y = \cos x$, and $y = \tan x$. III

Graph on the real number plane functions of the forms $y = a \sin bx$, $y = a \cos bx$, and $y = a \tan bx$. III

Define arc $\cos \frac{1}{2}$, inverse $\sin \frac{1}{2}$, $\tan^{-1} \frac{1}{2}$, and solve related problems. III

Define and graph the inverse circular functions of arc cos x, arc sin x, and arc tan x, and solve related problems. III

Solve open sentences that may require a substitution of the reciprocal, quotient, and Pythagorean identities. III

Solve open sentences that may require a substitution of any of the trigonometric identities. III

02-020-020 **Use vectors, polar coordinates, and the polar form of complex numbers to find the solutions to analytic problems. III**

Define *vector, equivalent vectors, the sense of vectors,* and *zero vectors.* II

Multiply a vector by a real number (scalar multiplication). II

Add and subtract vectors. II

Verify that addition of vectors is commutative and associative, and that scalar multiplication is distributive over addition: $a(\vec{b} + \vec{c}) = \vec{ab} + \vec{ac}$. (These are not proofs.) II

Write related vector problems from word problems and solve them. III

Express in four different ways the same ordered pair (r, θ), where r is the polar distance and θ is the direction angle. II

In the domain of real numbers, convert a point $P(x, y)$ in the rectangular-coordinate system to an equivalent point $P(r, \theta)$ in the polar-coordinate system, and vice versa.   II

Given the vector 2/30°, find the rectangular components. Given the rectangular components, find the direction angle and/or the radius vector.   II

From the conversion formulas $x = r \cos \theta$ and $y = r \sin \theta$, derive the polar form $[r(\cos \theta + i \sin \theta)]$ of a complex number $(x + yi)$, and vice versa.   II

Multiply two complex numbers that are written in the polar form $r(\cos \theta)$.   II

Divide two complex numbers that are written in the polar form.   II

Find and write the powers and roots of complex numbers that are written in polar form (De Moivre's theorem).   II

Derive the trigonometric series for the sin x and cos x, given the exponential series

$$\lim_{n \to \infty} \left(1 + \frac{x}{n}\right)^n = 1 + x + \frac{x^2}{2!} + \frac{x^3}{3!} + \frac{x^4}{4!} \cdot \cdot \cdot = e^x$$

and from De Moivre's theorem

$$\cos x + i \sin x = \left(\cos \frac{x}{n} + i \sin \frac{x}{n}\right)^n$$

where $r = 1$ and n is a positive number. Use these series to solve related problems.   III

02-020-025   Graph plane curves specified in rectangular or polar coordinates, including those given by parametric equations.   III

Use each of the following to graph curves: symmetry, tangents to a curve at the origin, horizontal and vertical asymptotes, empty bands, intercepts.   III

Graph compound curves by using the addition-of-ordinates or product-of-ordinates method.   III

Recognize and graph curves given by parametric equations, and be able to eliminate the parameter. III

Recognize and graph special curves given in parametric form (e.g., cycloid, hypocycloid, epicycloid). III

Given an equation in rectangular coordinates, find an equivalent polar equation. Given a polar equation, find an equivalent rectangular equation. II

Solve problems related to the polar form of lines and circles, and rotate polar curves that contain only the cosine of 90°, 180°, or 270°. III

Recognize the polar form of the parabola, the ellipse, and the hyperbola, and draw them. II

Graph polar curves by using each of the following: symmetry, tangents at the origin, possible values of r, charts of polar curves, rotation theorem. III

02-020-030 **Find the derivative of an algebraic, trigonometric, inverse trigonometric, exponential, or logarithmic function, and develop formulas for these and other types of functions. V**

Define the derivative of a function, and identify common notations for it. I

Using the definition of *derivative*, find the derivative (if it exists) of a given rational function. II

Using the definition of *derivative*, develop formulas for differentiating the following types of functions. V
1. $y = x^n$, where n is a positive integer.
2. $y = cu$, where c is a constant and u is a differentiable function.
3. $y = u + v$, where u and v are differentiable functions.
4. $y = u \cdot v$, where u and v are differentiable functions.
5. $y = \dfrac{u}{v}$, where u and v are differentiable functions.

Using the appropriate formula, determine the derivative of given functions of the following types.   III
1. $y = u + v$, where u and v are differentiable functions.
2. $y = u \cdot v$, where u and v are differentiable functions.
3. $y = \dfrac{u}{v}$, where u and v are differentiable functions.

Use the chain rule to determine the derivative of a composite function.   III

Differentiate a given function defined implicitly.   III

Given an incomplete proof of the derivation of the formula for $\dfrac{d}{du}$ (sin u), find the missing details.   II

Given a composite trigonometric function (sine, cosine, or tangent), find its derivative.   II

Given an inverse trigonometric function (arc sin, arc cos, or arc tan), find its derivative.   II

Determine $\dfrac{dy}{dx}$ or $\dfrac{d^2y}{dx^2}$ where x and y are expressed parametrically as functions of a third variable.   III

Find the derivative of a function of the form $y = \ln u$, where u is a differentiable function of x.   II

Find the derivative of a function of the form $y = e^u$, where u is a differentiable function of x.   II

Use logarithmic differentiation to find the derivative of a function of the form $y = v^u$, where u and v are both differentiable functions of x.   III

Find the derivative of a function of the form $y = a^u$, where u is a differentiable function of x.   II

Algebra

02-025-005 **Define and use terms appropriate to set notation, and use set theory in solving problems. III**

Translate verbal descriptions of sets into set notation and, given a set in set notation, give its verbal description. III

List subsets of infinite sets and subsets of finite sets. I

Graph a set of numbers on a number line. III

Select the roster of a set whose members belong to a given universal set, and satisfy some stated condition. I

Given a universal set and a linear equation in two variables ($x + y = a$, where $a \, \epsilon \, 1$), select the correct solution set. I

Select from a list each compound inequality that has the empty set or the universe as its solution set. I

Given two sets, P and Q, select from a list their Cartesian product, $P \times Q$. I

Given two sets, M and N, select from a list a set of ordered pairs that is *not* a relation in $M \times N$. I

List all the subsets for a given set, two disjoint sets for a given universal set, and complement of a given set A for a given universal set. I

For two given sets, determine whether one is a subset of the other, a proper subset of the other, or a complement of the other with respect to a given universal set, and decide whether the two sets represent two disjoint sets. III .

Define and give the proper notations for the following: *subset, proper subset, universal set, empty set, complement of a set, disjoint sets, finite set, infinite set.* I

Given a replacement set for a variable, determine the truth set of an open sentence by substitution. III

Given the replacement set for the variable in an open sentence, graph the truth set.   III

Graph truth sets of open sentences, including sentences that have an absolute value in them.   III

02-025-010   Use Venn diagrams to represent relationships of sets.   III

Use Venn diagrams to represent the following: a given universal set, subsets of a given set, two disjoint sets, a given set and its complement, the union of two sets, the intersection of two sets.   III

Use Venn diagrams to demonstrate the following: the complement of the union of two sets, the complement of the intersection of two sets, the statement A ∩ B = A ∪ B, the statement A ∪ B = A ∩ B.   III

02-025-015   Solve simple linear equations and related word problems.   III

Find the value of a given algebraic expression that represents one or more operations.   II

Using the trial and error method, solve an equation.   III

Using the method of applying the inverse operation, solve an equation that involves one operation.   III

Solve an equation that involves more than one indicated operation.   III

Solve an equation that involves like terms.   III

Translate given word problems into simple equations, and solve the problems.   III

02-025-020   Solve simple word problems that involve the basic operations on integers, fractions, and decimals by using algebraic equations.   III

Use equations to solve word problems that involve addition, subtraction, multiplication, and division.   III

Use equations to solve word problems that involve addition, subtraction, multiplication, and division of common fractions. III

Use equations to solve word problems that involve addition, subtraction, multiplication, and division of decimal fractions. III

Express a common fraction or a decimal fraction as a percent, and write a percent as a decimal fraction or a common fraction. II

Use appropriate algebraic expressions to translate word problems into equations. III

Use algebraic equations to solve word problems that involve percent. III

Solve word problems that contain one unknown by writing and solving equations. II

Write an equation to find the missing term in a proportion, and solve a problem that can be represented by a proportion. III

Use proportions to solve problems that involve percents. III

Using the definition of subtraction, $a - b = a + (-b)$, find the difference of two integers. II

Using the following definition, find the quotient of any two integers: "A rational number is one that can be expressed as the quotient of two integers $\left(\dfrac{a}{b}, b \neq 0\right)$." II

02-025-025 **Recognize basic axioms and properties of operations, and use them in solving equations. III**

Identify examples of the following properties and, given an example, identify the property: closure properties of addition and multiplication, commutative properties of addition and multiplication, associative properties of addition and multiplication. I

Identity the distributive property and use it to combine terms.   I

Choose an equation that illustrates the distributive property.   I

Given a set of equations, select the one that is (or the one that is not) an identity.   I

Given algebraic statements of the axioms for multiplication of natural numbers, match each with the name of the axiom.   I

02-025-030   Develop an original finite mathematical system, defining elements and properties.   V

Devise a set of elements for an original finite mathematical system, and define an operation on the set.   V

If your set is closed under your operation, define another operation for which your set is not closed. If your set is not closed, define another operation for which your set is closed.   II

Choose three elements from each system you have defined, and find whether the associative principle holds.   II

Demonstrate the existence or nonexistence of the commutative principle for the two operations you have defined.   III

Identify and demonstrate an identity element (if one exists) for each of the operations you have defined.   III

Demonstrate the existence or nonexistence of an inverse for each element in your system for the two operations you have defined.   III

Identify and demonstrate the inverse of each element (if it exists) for a defined operation other than addition, subtraction, multiplication, or division for a given finite mathematical system.   III

Demonstrate that the commutative principle exists or does not exist for a defined operation other than addition, subtraction, multiplication, or division in a given finite mathematical system.   III

02-025-035   Perform basic operations on monomials, binomials, and polynomials, and solve related problems.   III

Add and subtract monomials.   II

Find the product of two monomials.   II

Find the quotient of two monomials.   II

Multiply a binomial by a monomial.   II

Find the product of two binomials, using the distributive property.   III

Add and subtract polynomials.   II

Find the product of a binomial and a trinomial.   II

Divide a polynomial by a polynomial.   II

Given three indicated binomial products, expand and find the ones that have the same middle term.   III

Solve word problems that involve multiplication of polynomials.   III

Given a polynomial in one variable with a degree of 2 and with a leading coefficient of -1, evaluate the polynomial for a given replacement of the variable.   III

Select, from a list of equations, the equation that gives the product of a monomial and a polynomial.   I

Given a polynomial, combine like terms to obtain a polynomial in simple form.   III

Find the sum of two polynomials by combining like terms.   III

Find the difference between two polynomials by using the definition of the negative of a polynomial and then combining like terms.   III

Given a polynomial with a degree of 3 or greater and with a list of possible binomial factors, find the binomial that is a factor of the polynomial, using long division.   II

Given an expression containing products, sums, and a quotient of polynomials, find the simplest form.   II

Given a set of three expressions that contain sums and products of polynomials, evaluate each for a given replacement of the variable.   II

Reduce a numerical expression that contains operators and grouping symbols to its simplest form.   II

Given the sum or the difference of two numbers and representing one of the numbers as x, write the other number.   II

02-025-040   Perform basic algebraic operations and simplifications that include factoring.   III

Add and subtract algebraic expressions.   II

Using the definition of subtraction, $a - b = a + (-b)$, find the difference of two integers.   II

Using the following definition, find the quotient of any two integers: "A rational number is one that can be expressed as the quotient of two integers $\left(\frac{a}{b}, b \neq 0\right)$."   II

Add and subtract polynomials.   II

Using the rules $a^n \cdot a^m = a^{m+n}$ and $(ab)^n = a^n b^n$, simplify algebraic expressions.   II

Multiply polynomials by monomials.   II

Using the distributive property, multiply polynomials by polynomials or expand powers of polynomials.   II

Using the following law of exponents, divide a monomial by a monomial: $\frac{a^n}{a^m} = a^{n-m}$, where $n \geqslant m$ and n and m are whole numbers. II

Divide a polynomial by a polynomial. II

Find the greatest common monomial factor of a polynomial. II

Using the sentence $a^2 - b^2 = (a + b)(a - b)$, find the difference of two squares as a product of a sum and a difference and find the product of a sum and a difference as the difference of two squares. II

Select from a list the greatest common factor of three given terms. I

Select from a list the correct factorization of a quadratic trinomial into its greatest common factor and a simpler trinomial. I

Multiply and divide algebraic expressions. II

Use the multiplication property of one to simplify rational algebraic expressions. III

Using the sentences $(a + b)^2 = a^2 + 2ab + b^2$ and $(a - b)^2 = a^2 - 2ab + b^2$, factor and expand binomials. II

Find the product of any two binomials mentally, and factor any trinomial that is factorable over the integers. II

Find the prime factors of trinomials. II

Define an algebraic fraction, and recognize the restrictions placed on the variables in the denominator. II

Simplify (reduce) algebraic fractions. II

Find the product of two algebraic fractions. II

Find the quotient of two algebraic fractions. II

Add and subtract algebraic fractions.   II

Given any two rational numbers in fractional form, find a rational number that is between them.   II

Write common fractions as repeating decimals and repeating decimals as common fractions.   II

Using the rules of radicals, simplify radicals. Using square-root tables or approximation methods, find the square root of a given number.   II

Simplify radicals that involve multiplication or division.   II

Simplify radicals that involve addition or subtraction.   II

Using the conjugate of a number, simplify expressions that contain radicals.   II

Using the fundamental order of operations, simplify numerical expressions.   II

02-025-045   Solve word problems by factoring polynomials.   III

Find the product of any two binomials mentally, and factor any trinomial that is factorable over the integers.   II

Factor trinomials.   I

Using the theorem $ab = 0$ if and only if $a = 0$ or $b = 0$, solve equations that are factorable.   III

Solve word problems that involve factorable quadratic equations.   III

Given an equation of the form $x^2 + bx + c = 0$, solve by factoring and select the sum of the roots from a list.   III

Select from a list the incorrect factorization of the difference of two squares.   I

Given a list of polynomials of several factoring types and proposed factorizations, select the incorrect factorization. I

Factor the special expressions $a^2 - b^2$, $a^2 + 2ab + b^2$, $a^2 - 2ab + b^2$, $a^3 + b^3$, and $a^3 - b^3$. II

Given two different polynomials, write their greatest common factor (GCF) and their least common multiple (LCM) by using the prime-factorization method. II

Factor quadratic trinomials over the real numbers. II

Solve quadrant equations and quadratic inequations (inequalities) by factoring or graphing. III

Solve problems by using factorial notation. III

Using the factor theorem and/or remainder theorem, determine and write factors, remainders, or roots that are associated with a given polynomial. III

Using the rules $a^n \cdot a^m = a^{m+n}$ and $(ab)^n = a^n b^n$, simplify algebraic expressions. II

Using the distributive property, multiply polynomials by polynomials (expand powers of polynomials). II

Determine the greatest common monomial factor of a polynomial. III

Given $(x + a)(x + b) = 0$, select from a list the only conclusion that can be drawn by applying the zero-factor rule. I

Given a uniform-motion problem, write an equation that can be used to solve the problem. III

02-025-050 **Solve equations by performing operations that involve algebraic fractions. III**

Define an algebraic fraction, and list the restrictions placed on the variables in the denominator. I

Find the simple form of algebraic fractions. II

Simplify algebraic fractions, using the rules for changing signs in pairs.   II

Given two algebraic fractions, find the product and express the answer in simple form.   II

Find the quotient of two algebraic fractions.   II

Find the sum of two algebraic fractions.   II

Find the sum of a fractional term and a nonfractional term.   II

Find the simple form of an algebraic complex fraction.   II

Solve fractional equations.   III

Solve a problem that involves the use of a fractional equation.   III

Write common fractions as repeating decimals and repeating decimals as common fractions.   II

02-025-055   Use algebraic equations to solve problems that involve ratio and proportion.   III

Separate a quantity into parts according to a given ratio.   II

Use the cross-product rule to solve a proportion.   III

Given a pair of numbers that belong to a direct variation, find the constant of proportionality. Use the constant of proportionality to find additional pairs of numbers in the same direct variation.   III

Solve direct-variation problems.   III

Solve inverse-variation problems.   III

Solve combined variation problems.   III

02-025-060 **Apply the rules of radicals and exponents to solve word problems. III**

Using the rules of radicals, simplify radicals. Using square-root tables or approximation methods, find the square root of a given number. II

Simplify radicals that involve multiplication or division. II

Simplify radicals that involve addition or subtraction. II

Solve equations that contain radicals. III

Given three equations of the form $x^2 - a = 0$, where a represents an integer, select the one(s) that have irrational roots. II

Simplify radicals by using the theorems about products, quotients, and powers of radicals. II

Simplify sums of radicals and products of sums that contain radicals. II

Solve quadratic inequalities and equations that contain radicals. III

Use the multiplication rule for radicals to simplify numerals of the form $\sqrt{a^2b^2}$. III

Find the simple form of a radical of the type $\sqrt{a/b}$, where a and b are integers. II

Find the simple form of a radical whose radicand has one factor that is a square and one that is not. II

Find the sum of three radicals. II

Find the simple form of a radical with a fractional radicand. II

Find the simple form of an expression like $(a + b \sqrt{c})/d$. II

Using the discriminant of a quadratic equation, tell whether the equation has one rational root, two rational roots, two irrational roots, or no real roots.   II

Solve an equation that contains the variable under a radical sign.   III

Solve word problems that require the use of exponents and radicals.   III

Using the following law of exponents, divide a monomial by a monomial: $\dfrac{a^n}{a^m} = a^{n-m}$.   II

Given a list of equations containing products, quotients, and powers of x, select the one that is (or the one that is not) a correct application of the axioms for exponents.   II

Given a list of equations containing negative and fractional exponents, select the one that *is not* a valid application of the axioms for exponents.   II

Simplify expressions with nonpositive integral exponents.   II

Solve word problems that are solvable by the use of the Pythagorean theorem.   III

02-025-065   Identify inequalities and express them through axioms, graphs, or sketches.   III

Given $a > b$, where a and b represent integers, select from a list of inequalities the one that does or the one that does not follow from the addition axiom for inequalities.   II

Given $a > b$, where a and b represent integers, select from a list of inequalities those that follow from the multiplication axioms for inequalities or those that do not.   II

Given an inequality of the form $ax + b > c$, where a, b, c are integers, find an equivalent inequality of the form $x > d$.   II

Given a linear inequality of the type $ax + b > cx + d$, where $a < c$, find an equivalent inequality whose left member is x.   II

Select from a list the graph of an inequality of the form $x > a$ or of the form $x \geq a$.   II

Demonstrate $A \times B = B \times A$ for given sets A and B where $A = B$, and demonstrate $A \times B \neq B \times A$ for given sets A and B where $A \neq B$.   III

Sketch the graph of a compound inequality $x < a$ or $x > b$, where $a < b$.   III

Sketch the graph of a compound inequality $x > a$ and $x < b$, where $a < b$.   III

Given an inequality that contains absolute value symbols, $|x - a| < d$ or $|x - a| > d$, find an equivalent compound inequality that does not contain absolute value symbols.   II

Sketch the graph of the statement $x > a$ and $x > b$ or the statement $x > a$ or $x > b$.   III

Select from a list the compound inequality that is represented by a graph.   I

Select the inequality that corresponds to a given graph, or graph a given inequality.   I

Solve simple inequalities and graph the solutions.   III

Solve compound inequalities and graph the solution sets.   III

02-025-070   **Solve word problems that involve simultaneous equations.   III**

Given an equation of the form $a^n = b$, where a and b are integers and n is a natural number, find an equivalent statement that uses the word *root*.   II

Given a pair of equations, select the postulate that makes the second equation equivalent to the first.   I

Given two equations of the form $a(x + b) = c$, where a, b, c are integers, solve each and find the sum of the roots. III

Given two equations of the form $ax + b = cx + d$, where a, b, c, and d are integers, solve each and find the sum of the roots. III

Given the total cost of a given number of units, each having either one of two possible prices, write the equation that can be used to find the number of units having each value. III

Given a problem that involves two variables and two conditions, select a system of equations that will produce a solution. I

Solve problems that involve systems of two equations in two variables. III

Given a linear equation in one variable of the type $ax + b = c$, $ax + bx = c$, or $a(x + b) = c$, where a, b, and c are integers, select the first step in the procedure for solving. I

Given three linear equations of the form $ax + b = c$, solve each and find the sum of the three roots. III

Solve a system of two linear equations in two variables. III

Solve word problems that involve systems of two simultaneous linear equations. III

Given a base–rate–percentage problem in which two quantities are computed at different rates and in which only the totals are known, find the two quantities. II

02-025-075 Solve word problems that involve quadratic equations. III

Solve quadratic equations that can be written in the form $(x = a)^2 = b^2$, where a and b are real numbers. III

If the roots of $ax^2 + bx + c = 0$ are r_1 and r_2, determine the relationships between the coefficients a, b, and c and the roots r_1 and r_2.   III

Solve quadratic equations by completing the square.   III

Given $ax^2 + bx + c = 0$, derive a quadratic formula for x where x is a real number.   III

Determine the discriminant of a quadratic equation, and use it to determine the nature of the roots.   III

Solve word problems by using the quadratic formula.   III

Graph the truth set of quadratic inequalities.   III

Solve quadratic-quadratic systems.   III

Given a quadratic equation of the form $ax^2 + bx + c = 0$ (where a, b, and c are integers), find the roots by substitution.   II

Given a quadratic equation of the form $x^2 + bx + c = 0$ and one factor, find the other.   II

Given three quadratic polynomials, determine which ones have the same factor.   III

Select from a list the missing term of a quadratic trinomial that would make the trinomial the square of a binomial.   I

Solve word problems by using a quadratic equation.   III

Convert a quadratic equation to standard form.   III

Use the quadratic formula to find the roots of a quadratic equation.   III

Prove the binomial theorem by mathematical induction, and use the results to solve related problems.   III

Expand a binomial such as $(a + b)^n$, where n is an integer less than 10.   III

Use mathematical induction to prove or disprove conjectures about the natural numbers.   III

Determine the roots of a polynomial equation with real coefficients, using Descartes' rule of signs and this theorem: "If a polynomial equation with real coefficients has $a + bi$ as a root (a and b real, $b \neq 0$), then $a - bi$ is also a root."   III

Use the numerical coefficients of an equation with integral coefficients to determine and write all of the possible rational roots.   III

Given any quadratic equation with real coefficients and using the relations between roots, coefficients, and the discriminant, write the nature of the roots, the sum of the roots, and the product of the roots.   III

02-025-080   Solve equations and inequalities that include linear and quadratic systems and polynomial equations.   III

Rewrite verbal descriptions of sets into set notation and, given a set in set notation, give its verbal description.   II

Recognize subsets of infinite sets and subsets of finite sets.   II

Solve algebraic expressions for various values of the variable.   III

Given a replacement set for a variable, find the truth set of an open sentence by substitution.   II

Use the following property to solve equations: If a, b, and c are real numbers and $a = b$, then $a + c = b + c$ and $a - c = b - c$.   III

Use the following property to solve equations: If a, b, and c ($c \neq 0$) are real numbers and $a = b$, then $ac = bc$ and $\frac{a}{c} = \frac{b}{c}$.   III

Solve equations that contain rational numbers.   III

Given the following properties, use them to recognize relationships about numbers. III
1. If $a < b$, then $a + c = b$ for some $c > 0$.
2. If $a < b$, then $a + c < b + c$ for all c.
3. If $a < b$, then $\dfrac{a}{c} < \dfrac{b}{c}$ if $c > 0$.
4. If $a < b$, $b < c$, then $a < c$.

Solve simple and compound inequalities, and graph the solution sets. III

Using the theorem $ab = 0$ if and only if $a = 0$ or $b = 0$, solve equations that are factorable. III

Solve fractional equations. III

Using the addition or subtraction method, solve a system of two simultaneous linear equations. III

Solve equations that contain radicals. III

Solve quadratic equations that can be written in the form $(x - a)^2 = b^2$, where a and b are real numbers. III

If the roots of $ax^2 + bx + c = 0$ are r_1 and r_2, find the relationships between the coefficients a, b, and c and r_1 and r_2. II

Solve quadratic equations by completing the square. III

Given $ax^2 + bx + c = 0$, find a quadratic formula for x where x is a real number. II

Find the discriminant of a quadratic equation and use it to determine the nature of the roots. III

02-025-085 **Explain the difference between arithmetic and geometric progression, and solve related problems. III**

Calculate and write the arithmetic mean of two terms in an arithmetic progression. II

Determine the formula for the sum of an arithmetic progression (a series), and write the sum for a given number of terms in an arithmetic series. III

Solve word problems by using arithmetic progressions. III

Derive the formula for the nth term of a geometric progression (GP), and write the nth term of a given geometric progression. III

Write the geometric mean of two terms in a geometric progression. II

Derive the formula for the sum of a geometric progression (a series), and write the sum for a given number of terms in a geometric series. III

Derive the formula for an infinite geometric series, and find the sum of an infinite geometric series. III

Solve word problems by using geometric series. III

02-025-090   Solve problems that require the use of properties of arithmetic, geometric, and binomial expansions. III

Derive the formula for the nth term of an arithmetic progression. III

Find the nth term of a given arithmetic progression. II

Calculate and write the arithmetic mean between two terms of an arithmetic progression. II

Derive the formula for the sum of an arithmetic progression, and find the sum for a given number of terms in an arithmetic series. III

Solve word problems by using arithmetic progressions. III

Derive the formula for the nth term of a geometric progression, and find the nth term of a given geometric progression. III

Find the geometric mean of two terms in a geometric progression. II

Derive the formula for the sum of a geometric progression, and find the sum for a given number of terms in a geometric series. III

Derive the formula for an infinite geometric series, and find the sum of an infinite geometric series. III

Solve word problems by using geometric series. III

Solve problems by using factorial notation. III

Expand binomials such as $(a + b)^n$, where n is an integer less than 10. III

Find any term of a binomial expansion by using the binomial theorem. II

Prove the binomial theorem by mathematical induction, and use the results to solve related problems. III

02-025-095 **Solve problems that require the use of properties of real numbers or of complex numbers. III**

Express rational numbers as repeating or terminating decimals and vice versa. II

Find an irrational number between any two real numbers. II

Recognize examples of the following properties and, given an example, recognize the property: closure properties of addition and multiplication, commutative properties of addition and multiplication, associative properties of addition and multiplication. II

Recognize the distributive property, and use it to combine like terms. II

Write formal proofs of real-number theorems by using the properties of real numbers. III

Find decimal approximations for irrational numbers by graphing and by using tables. II

Considering the standard form $a + bi$, where a and b are real numbers, describe the conditions for which two complex numbers are equal.   II

Add, subtract, and multiply complex numbers of the form $a + bi$.   II

Find the conjugates of complex numbers, and use them in dividing complex numbers.   II

Given complex numbers of the form $a + bi$, find the identity element and the additive inverse. Demonstrate with examples that the associative and commutative properties of addition and multiplication should hold for complex numbers of the form $a + bi$ and that the distributive property of multiplication over addition also holds.   III

Determine whether the roots of the equation $ax^2 + bx + c = 0$ (a, b, and c are real numbers) are complex by using the discriminant. If they are complex, determine the graph of the equation on the real plane. Solve equations with complex coefficients.   III

Find the sum of and difference between complex numbers graphically.   II

Simplify numerical expressions that involve the four basic operations on real numbers.   II

Determine the conjugates of complex numbers, and use them in dividing complex numbers.   III

Given complex numbers of the form $(a + bi)$, determine the identity element and the additive inverse. Show by using examples that the associative and commutative properties of addition and multiplication hold and that the distributive property of multiplication over addition also holds.   III

Define the following terms as related to the concept of proof: *axioms (postulates), definitions, reflexive, symmetric, transitive, substitution, theorem, equivalence.*   I

Solve equations and simplify algebraic expressions with real numbers as exponents.   III

02-025-100   Classify numbers as rational or irrational.   II

Given a number line and a set of rational numbers, write the numbers on the number line.   II

Given a description of a set of rational numbers, express that set by using set notation.   II

Using the method of averaging, find the rational number that is halfway between any two given rational numbers.   II

Define real numbers, and classify given real numbers as rational or irrational.   II

Find the product, quotient, sum, and difference of rational numbers.   II

Write rational numbers as repeating or terminating decimals, and vice versa.   II

Locate and write an irrational number between any two real numbers.   II

Given any two numbers in fractional form, find a rational number that is between them.   II

Locate decimal approximations for irrational numbers by graphing and by using tables.   II

02-025-105   Perform complex algebraic operations and simplifications.   III

Simplify numerical expressions that involve the four basic operations on real numbers.   II

Simplify polynomials by using the basic laws of positive integral exponents.   II

Multiply polynomials over the real numbers.   II

Factor these special expressions: $a^2 - b^2$; $a^2 + 2ab + b^2$; $a^2 - 2ab + b^2$; $a^3 + b^3$; $a^3 - b^3$. II

Given two different polynomials, express their greatest common factor and their least common multiple by using the prime-factorization method. II

Factor quadratic trinomials over the real numbers. II

Simplify expressions with nonpositive integral exponents. II

Rewrite expressions as rational algebraic expressions with the correct restrictions on the variables. II

Use the multiplication property of 1 to simplify rational algebraic expressions. II

Multiply and divide algebraic expressions. II

Find the sum and difference of algebraic expressions. II

Simplify complex fractions. II

Simplify radicals by using the theorems about products, quotients, and powers of radicals. II

Simplify sums of radicals and products of sums containing radicals. II

Given a set of five integers, find the sum when a given integer is added to each. II

Given a set of five integers, find the difference when each is subtracted from a given integer. II

Given a set of five integers, find the products (or quotients) when a given integer is used as multiplier (or divisor). II

Calculate $a^m b^n$, where a and b are integers and m and n are positive integers less than 6. II

Given two integers, $a \neq b$, define the relation between them by using the greater-than or the less-than symbol. I

02-025-110 Graph relations and functions. III

Find and graph the Cartesian product $(A \times B)$ for given sets A and B where sets A and B are composed of integers only. III

Define $A \times B = B \times A$ for given sets A and B where $A = B$. Define $A \times B \neq B \times A$ for given sets A and B where $A \neq B$. I

Given a simple mathematical sentence that involves rational numbers such as $n > 2$, graph the solution set for n on a number line. III

Given a compound sentence such as $n < 15$ and $n \geqslant \dfrac{2}{5}$, graph its solution set on a number line. III

Given sets A and B where $n(A) \leq 6$ and $n(B) \leq 6$, find and graph a relation defined by a given rule and a given domain. III

Express a given relation by using a mathematical sentence. II

Recognize whether a given relation is also a function. II

Graph the relation or the function defined by a given mathematical sentence and a given domain D where D is restricted to integers and $n(D) \leqslant 10$. III

Given a list of relations, select the one that is a function. I

Use the vertical-line test to determine whether a graph represents a function. III

Given the defining equation and the domain, select the range of a function from a list of sets. II

Find the maximum or minimum of a quadratic function. II

Solve an area problem, using the maximum value of a function. II

Use the maximum value of a quadratic function to solve a pricing problem. III

Using special notation such as $f(x)$, solve problems that involve functions. III

Solve direct variation problems by using facts about linear functions. III

Graph equations of straight lines. III

Solve first-degree systems of n equations in n unknowns for $n \leq 4$. III

List the conditions for which two lines are perpendicular. I

Graph relations and list equations for relations. III

Identify functions, and graph the functions you have identified. III

Graph a relation on the coordinate plane that is defined by a set of ordered pairs or an open sentence. III

Given an equation of a line, the graph of a line, or any two points of a line, derive the slope. III

Given two points that lie on a line, or one point and the slope, determine the equation of the line. III

Find and graph the Cartesian product $(A \times B)$ for given sets A and B where sets A and B are composed of integers only. III

Using the ideas of the Cartesian product or the fundamental counting principle, solve problems that involve permutations for n objects that are all different. III

02-025-115 Graph truth sets of quadratic equations and inequalities, and graph functions and relations. III

Graph a set of numbers on a number line. III

Given the replacement set for the variable in an open sentence, graph the truth set. III

Graph truth sets of open sentences, including sentences that have absolute value. III

Given a linear equation in two variables, construct its graph. III

Given any two points on a nonvertical line, write the equation of the line and find its slope. III

Given an inequality with linear terms, construct its graph. III

Graph systems of inequalities in two variables. III

Graph relations and write equations for relations. III

Recognize functions and graph functions. III

Graph the truth set of quadratic inequalities. III

Graph systems of equations with at least one quadratic equation. III

02-025-120 **Graph relations and functions, and find equations of relations and functions, both linear and quadratic. III**

Graph a relation on the coordinate plane that is defined by a set of ordered pairs or an open sentence. III

Graph equations of straight lines. III

Given two points that lie on a line, or one point and the slope, find the equation of the line. II

Graph quadratic inequalities. III

Use the distance formula to find the distance between any two points in the plane. III

Given the center and the radius of a circle, express the equation of the circle and graph it. III

Given an equation of a circle in the form $ax^2 + ay^2 + bx + cy + F = 0$, express the equation in the form $(x - h)^2 + (y - k)^2 = r^2$ (center–radius form). II

Given the directrix, the focus, and the definition of a parabola, find the equation of the parabola. II

Given the foci and definition of an ellipse, find its equation. II

Find the equation of a hyperbola from its definitions and graph it. II

Given a linear equation in two variables, draw its graph. III

Given any two points on a nonvertical line, write the equation of the line and determine its slope. III

Given an inequality with linear terms, draw its graph. III

Using the addition or subtraction method, solve a system of two simultaneous linear equations. III

Graph systems of inequalities in two variables. III

Given a graph of four points, determine their coordinates. III

Given a set of points, select from a list the equation their coordinates satisfy. I

Find the slope of a line segment, given the coordinates of its endpoints. II

Find the equation of the line passing through two given points. II

Given an equation of the form $y = mx + b$, find the graph of the equation. II

Given the standard form of a linear equation, find the slope–intercept form. II

Given a linear equation in two variables of the form $Ax + By = C$, where A and B each divide C, find both intercepts of the equation.   II

Given a system of linear equations in two variables where one equation has a term with a coefficient of 1, solve the system by using the substitution method.   III

Given a system of equations, tell whether the graph is a pair of intersecting, parallel, or coinciding lines.   II

Advanced Math

02-030-005 **Use equations and graphs to solve problems related to conic sections.** III

Define *focus, parabola, ellipse,* and *hyperbola.* I

Given the center and the radius of a circle, write the equation of the circle and draw its graph. III

Given an equation of a circle in the form $ax^2 + ay^2 + bx + cy + F = 0$, write the equation in the form $(x - h)^2 + (y - k)^2 = r^2$ (center–radius form). II

Given the directrix, the focus, and the definition of *parabola,* write the equation of the parabola. II

Given the equation of a parabola, $y = a(x - h)^2 + k$, where a, h, k are constants, find the vertex, the y intercept, and the point that is symmetrically opposite the y intercept. III

Given the foci and definition of *ellipse,* write its equation. II

Write the equation of a hyperbola from its definition, and draw its graph. III

Graph the equation for an equilateral hyperbola that is also an inverse variation. III

Use the distance formula to determine the distance between any two points in the plane. III

02-030-010 **Solve problems by using matrices.** III

Solve a 2 × 2 system of linear equations by using matrices. III

Solve systems of linear equations by using matrix transformations. III

02-030-015 **Combine principles, concepts, and generalizations by developing an original finite mathematical system, by listing a set of elements, and by defining an operation on the set for which the set is closed and one for which the set is not closed. V**

Develop an original finite mathematical system by listing a set of elements and by defining an operation on the set for which the set is closed. V

Develop an original finite mathematical system by listing a set of elements and by defining an operation on the set for which the set is not closed. V

Demonstrate whether or not the associative principle holds for any three elements of an original finite mathematical system you have developed. V

Demonstrate the existence or nonexistence of the commutative principle for an operation on the set for which the set is closed in an original finite mathematical system, and an operation on the set for which the set is unclosed in an original finite mathematical system. V

Demonstrate the existence or nonexistence of an identity element for an operation on the set for which the set is closed in an original finite mathematical system, and an operation on the set for which the set is unclosed in an original finite mathematical system. V

Demonstrate the existence or nonexistence of an inverse for each element in the set for an operation on the set for which the set is closed in an original finite mathematical system, and an operation on the set for which the set is unclosed in an original finite mathematical system. V

Solve problems by using binary operations other than addition, subtraction, multiplication, and division. III

Solve division of fraction problems by using multiplicative inversion. III

Recognize examples of the properties of commutativity, associativity, and distributivity. II

For a given set of numbers and a given operation, recognize whether the operation is closed for that set.   II

02-030-020   Solve problems that require the use of properties of exponential, logarithmic, linear, and quadratic functions, and make judgments regarding the efficiency of these functions in given problems.   VI

Using special notation such as $f(x)$, solve problems that involve functions.   III

Solve direct variation problems by using facts about linear functions.   III

Given an equation of a line, the graph of a line, or any two points of a line, find the slope.   III

Solve problems that involve quadratic functions specified by the equation $y = az^2$.   III

Find the vertex and axis of symmetry for any quadratic function specified by $y = a(x - h)^2 + k$.   III

Find the vertex, indicating whether it is maximum or minimum, and the axis of symmetry of any quadratic function specified by $y = ax^2 + bx + c$.   II

Given numbers in their exponential form, express them in their logarithmic form. Solve equations and simplify algebraic expressions that contain logarithms.   III

Find logarithms and antilogarithms of numbers by using tables and linear interpolation.   II

Given an exponential equation $x^n = N$, find an equivalent logarithmic equation.   II

Given a list of numbers and their supposed logarithms, find the item that contains an error.   II

Given a list of logarithms of products, quotients, powers, and roots, select the one that is in error.   I

Match a logarithmic equation with its corresponding arithmetic equation.   I

Apply logarithms to solve a compound-interest problem. III

Using theorems for logarithms of products and quotients, multiply and divide numbers and solve equations. III

Apply logarithms in evaluating exponential expressions, computing answers to word problems, and solving equations. III

Given the assessed value of property, find the property tax when the rate is expressed in dollars per $100 or per $1000 of assessed valuation. II

Given the assessed value of the property, find the property tax when the rate is expressed in mills or cents per $1.00 of assessed valuation or when the rate is expressed as a percent of the assessed valuation. II

Given the annual interest rate compounded daily, determine the interest on a specified amount of savings for a specified period of time. III

Given a payment schedule and the amount of a loan, determine the amount of interest on the loan. III

Use the formula $\mathrm{Log}_b N = \dfrac{\mathrm{Log}_c N}{\mathrm{Log}_c b}$ to solve exponential equations. III

Use logarithms to evaluate exponential expressions, compute answers to word problems, and solve equations. III

02-030-025 Find the derivative of an algebraic, trigonometric, inverse trigonometric, exponential, or logarithmic function. III

Solve quadratic equations and quadratic inequations (inequalities) by factoring or graphing. III

Determine and solve quadratic equations that are derived from word problems. III

Solve fractional equations and fractional inequations (inequalities). III

Solve word problems that involve fractional equations. III

Solve equations and inequalities that may or may not contain absolute values, and solve open sentences that are derived from word problems. III

Solve first degree systems of n equations in n unknowns for $n \leq 4$. III

Solve linear systems derived from word problems. III

Use the numerical coefficients of an equation with integral coefficients to find all of the possible rational roots. III

Solve quadratic equations by completing the square and by using the quadratic formula. III

Given any quadratic equation with real coefficients and using the relations between roots and coefficients and the discriminant, find the nature of the roots, the sum of the roots, and the product of the roots. II

Solve quadratic inequalities and equations containing radicals. III

Solve equations involving inverse variation. III

Solve linear-quadratic systems by the algebraic method. III

Solve quadratic-quadratic systems. III

Given a specific point, find the value of a polynomial function by synthetic substitution. II

Using the factor theorem and/or remainder theorem, find factors or remainders or roots that are associated with a given polynomial. II

Find the roots of a polynomial equation with real coefficients, using Descartes' rule of signs and this theorem: "If a polynomial equation with real coefficients has $a + bi$ as a root (a and b real, $b \neq 0$), then $a - bi$ is also a root." II

Graph a polynomial function through the use of synthetic substitution, a table of values, the property of continuity, and the change of signs. III

Find the integral lower and upper bounds for the roots of polynomial equations. II

02-030-030 Apply knowledge of the properties and functions and limits without reference to calculus. III

Define and use the following terms and notations: *relation, function, mapping, image, f(x), f:x → f(x), domain, range.* III

Given a relation, determine whether the graph describes a function, and solve problems related to the graphs of step functions and absolute value functions. III

Given a relation or function, determine whether its inverse exists, write or graph the inverse, and solve related problems. III

Given two or three rational functions, determine a particular composite function and solve related problems. III

Apply theorems about inverse functions to solve problems. III

Define the functions $y = \ln x$ and $y = e^x$ as inverse functions, and determine their properties. III

Using the properties of limits listed below, find limits where $F(t)$ and $G(t)$ are polynomials. II
1. $\lim\limits_{t \to a} [F(t) + G(t)] = \lim\limits_{t \to a} F(t) + \lim G(t)$
2. $\lim\limits_{t \to a} [kF(t)] = k \lim\limits_{t \to a} F(t)$
3. $\lim\limits_{t \to a} [F(t) \cdot G(t)] = \lim\limits_{t \to a} F(t) \cdot \lim G(t)$
4. $\lim\limits_{t \to a} \dfrac{F(t)}{G(t)} = \dfrac{\lim\limits_{t \to a} F(t)}{\lim\limits_{t \to a} G(t)}, \lim\limits_{t \to a} G(t) \neq 0$

Using the concept of a limit, find the slope of a given polynomial function at a given point. II

Using the definition of continuity, test a given function for continuity at a given point.   II

D2-030-035   Apply methods of calculus or numerical analysis to the approximation of functional values, transcendental functions, and definite integrals.   III

Demonstrate an understanding of differentials by interpreting them geometrically and by relating them to Δx and Δy.   III

Given an algebraic function, estimate the functional value for given values of x and Δx, using $\Delta y \approx \dfrac{dy}{dx} \Delta x$.   III

Using differentials, determine approximations to radicals and powers.   III

Using Newton's method, approximate the roots of a given algebraic equation.   III

Given a definite integral of a simple algebraic function, use the trapezoidal rule to determine an approximate numerical value.   III

Using Simpson's rule, determine an approximate numerical value of a given definite integral of an algebraic or a transcendental function.   III

Determine a polynomial function of degree n (where $n \leq 4$) whose graph passes through a given set of points.   III

Using polynomials, determine to a preassigned accuracy an approximate value of e^x for a given value of x near 0 or an approximate value of $\ln x$ for a given value of x near 1.   III

Using polynomials, determine to a preassigned accuracy an approximate value of $\sin x$ or of $\cos x$ for a given value of x.   III

02-030-040 **Derive the integral of an algebraic or transcendental function by using a basic integration formula or a standard technique of integration. III**

Using basic integration formulas, evaluate directly given integrals of the type $\int u^n du$, where n is an algebraic or a transcendental function and u is any number. III

Integrate a given trigonometric function that requires the substitution of a trigonometric identity. II

Using a trigonometric substitution, integrate a given algebraic function that involves the sum or difference of two squares. II

Using the method of partial fractions, integrate a given rational function. II

Integrate a given function by parts. II

02-030-045 **Show that you can apply integral calculus to the solution of practical problems from geometry, physics, or everyday life. III**

Apply integration to the problem of finding the area under a curve. III

Using integration, determine the area under a given curve or between two given curves. III

Using integration, determine the length of a given curve. III

Using integration, determine the volume of a given solid of revolution. III

Using integration, find the average value of a function over a given domain. II

Use integration in solving work problems from physics. III

Given the velocity or the acceleration as a function of time and given the initial conditions, apply indefinite integration to find distance as a function of time. III

Use the differential equation $y' = ky$ to solve word problems that involve growth or decay. III

02-030-050 Apply differential calculus to the solution of practical problems from geometry, physics, or everyday life. III

Using the concept of a limit, find the slope of a given polynomial function at a given point. II

Find the nth derivative of a given rational function. II

Graph a given function by using the first derivative to determine the direction of the curve and by using the first and second derivatives to locate relative maximum points, relative minimum points, and points of inflection. III

Using first and second derivatives, solve maximization and minimization problems. III

Using first and second derivatives, solve related rate and motion problems. III

Solve word problems that require the differentiation of trigonometric or inverse trigonometric functions. III

Given a function and the endpoints of an interval, determine a point c within the interval that satisfies the mean-value theorem. III

Given a specific point, evaluate a polynomial function by synthetic substitution. III

02-030-055 Construct derivations or proofs of differentiation formulas or of theorems of differential and integral calculus. III

Define the derivative of a function and identify common notations for it. I

Using the definition of *derivative,* develop formulas for differentiating the following types of functions.   III
1. $y = x^n$, where n is a positive integer.
2. $y = cu$, where c is a constant and u is a differentiable function.
3. $y = u + v$, where u and v are differentiable functions.
4. $y = u \cdot v$, where u and v are differentiable functions.
5. $y = \dfrac{u}{v}$, where u and v are differentiable functions.

Given an incomplete proof of the derivation of the formula for $\dfrac{d}{du}$ (sin u), find the missing details.   II

Given the formula for $\dfrac{d}{du}$ (sin u), find derivations for $\dfrac{d}{du}$ (cos u) and for $\dfrac{d}{du}$ (tan u).   II

Given an incomplete proof of the derivations for $\dfrac{d}{du}$ (arc sin u), $\dfrac{d}{du}$ (arc cos u), and $\dfrac{d}{du}$ (arc tan u), find the missing details.   II

Illustrate Rolle's theorem geometrically.   III

Illustrate the mean-value theorem geometrically.   III

Given an incomplete proof of the mean-value theorem, find the missing details.   II

Define *integration* to be the determination of an antiderivative.   II

Define *definite integral* to be the limit of a sum.   II

Prove and use the Fundamental Theorem of integral calculus.   III

Develop and use the following properties of the definite integral.   III

1. $\displaystyle\int_a^b [f(x) + g(x)]\, dx = \int_a^b f(x)\, dx + \int_a^b g(x)\, dx$

2. $\displaystyle\int_a^b cf(x)\, dx = c \int_a^b f(x)\, dx$

3. $\displaystyle\int_a^b f(x)\, dx = \int_a^c f(x)\, dx + \int_c^b f(x)\, dx$ where $a < c < b$

4. If $\displaystyle F(x) = \int_a^x f(t)\, dt$, then $F'(x) = f(x)$.

Statistics, Probability, Logic, and Computers

02-035-005 **Apply the frequencies and measures of central tendency. III**

Given a set of data, organize the data into intervals and, with tally marks, show the frequency of events. II

Given a set of data, find the arithmetic mean. III

Given a set of jumbled (unordered) data, find the median when interpolation is not required. III

Find the median of a set of data where interpolation is needed. III

Given a set of data, recognize the mode. II

Given a set of numerical data, find the average. III

02-035-010 **Demonstrate the theory of probability. III**

Define the following words: *likely, more likely, equal chances, certain, uncertain, impossible.* I

Using a fraction, express the probability of a given event. II

Using the notation P(E), express the probability of a given event E. II

Find P for a given event E. II

Using a tree diagram or a table, find all possible outcomes, and then find the probability of a given outcome. II

Find the probability for a compound event of the both/and type or for an event of the either/or type. II

Perform a probability experiment to count the number of ways the experiment can turn out. III

Find the number of ways that 2, 3, or 4 things can be chosen from n things ($n \leq 6$). II

Find the number of ways 2, 3, or 4 things can be arranged in a different order. II

Construct a tree diagram that shows the ways a probability experiment can turn out. III

Construct an array that shows the ways a probability experiment can turn out. III

Using a table of outcomes (an array), predict the result of a probability experiment. III

Perform a probability experiment that requires from 20 to 30 repeated trials, and record the result of each trial. III

Construct a table to show the results of several repetitions of a probability experiment. Construct a line graph or a bar graph to summarize the data. III

Given a bar graph that represents the results of a probability experiment, describe the data in a written report. II

Describe all the possible outcomes of an event. II

Find the probability for each outcome of an event if the outcomes are all equally likely. III

Find the probability for each outcome of an event if the outcomes are not all equally likely. III

Given two independent events, A and B, find the probability of a certain outcome of A and a certain outcome of B both occurring. III

Given the number of favorable events (desired outcomes) and the total number of possible events, find the probability of obtaining a given favorable event. III

Given the number of favorable events and the total number of possible events, find the probability of two given favorable events occurring successively. III

Given a specific random sample of population, recognize whether generalizations about it are justified. II

Using set notation, express all possible outcomes for a given experiment. II

Use set notation to express a specified event in a given sample space. II

Using the notation $P(E) = \dfrac{n(E)}{n(x)}$ where x = sample space, E = event, and P = probability, express the probabilities of n dimensional events ($n \leq 4$). III

Given $P(A)$ and using the principle $P(A) + P(\overline{A}) = 1$, find $P(\overline{A})$. II

Given the two events A and B, mutually exclusive or not, find the probability of $A \cup B$ by using the following formula. III

$$P(A \cup B) = \frac{n(A) + n(B) - n(A \cap B)}{n(\cup)}$$
$$= P(A) + P(B) - P(A \cap B).$$

Given events A and B, find whether they are independent by comparing $P(A \cap B)$ with $P(A) \cdot P(B)$. III

Given the two independent events A and B, find the probability of $(A \cap B)$ by using the formula $P(A \cap B) = P(A) \cdot P(B)$. III

Using Pascal's triangle, find the number of combinations of n things taken r at a time ($n \leq 10$). III

Find the probability of an event that involves permutations or combinations. III

02-035-015 Apply probability theory to solve word problems. III

Apply the concept of the Cartesian product or the fundamental counting principle to solve problems that involve permutations for n objects, all of which are different. III

Solve problems by using the formula for the number of permutations of n objects, not all of which are different. III

Derive the formula for finding the number of combinations of n elements taken r at a time $(_nC_r)$. III

Find the number of combinations of n elements taken r at a time $(_nC_r)$. II

Solve combination permutation word problems. III

Considering a sample space with outcomes equally likely, solve word problems that involve single-event probability. III

Solve word problems that involve the probability of mutually exclusive events. III

Solve word problems that involve the probability of independent and dependent events. III

List all possible outcomes for a given experiment. I

Given the formula $P = \dfrac{\text{number of favorable outcomes}}{\text{number of trials}}$, predict the outcome of favorable events. III

Given $P(E)$ and using the principle $P(E) + P(\overline{E}) = 1$, find $P(\overline{E})$. II

List specified events in a given sample space. I

02-035-020 Express relationships based on sets and set notation. III

Given a description of set, including the empty set, write its elements (members) by using set notation. II

Identify and tell the difference between equal sets and equivalent sets. I

Recognize all the subsets of a set. II

Describe the set that is the union of two given sets. II

Describe the set that is the intersection of two given sets. II

Tell the meaning and give proper notations for the following. I
1. subset
2. proper subset
3. universal set
4. empty set
5. complement of a set
6. disjoint sets
7. finite set
8. infinite set

Find (1) all the subsets for a given set, (2) two disjoint sets for a given universal set, and (3) the complement of a given set A for a given universal set. II

Determine which of the following relations describes two given sets. III
1. One is a subset of the other.
2. One is a proper subset of the other.
3. One is a complement of the other with respect to a given universal set.
4. The two sets represent two disjoint sets.

Given a description of a set of rational numbers, express that set by using set notation. II

Express the intersection of any three sets by using Venn diagrams. II

Using Venn diagrams, express the following: a given universal set, subsets of a given set, two disjoint sets, a given set and its complement, the union of two sets, the intersection of two sets. II

Using Venn diagrams, express the following: the complement of the union of two sets, the complement of the intersection of two sets, the statement $A \cap B = A \cup B$, the statement $A \cup B = A \cap B$. II

Using the notation $n(A)$ to represent the number of elements in set A, express the cardinality of given sets and combinations of sets. II

02-035-025   Combine principles, concepts, and generalizations by developing an original finite mathematical system, by listing a set of elements, and by defining an operation on the set for which the set is closed and one for which the set is not closed.   V

Develop an original finite mathematical system by listing a set of elements and by defining an operation on the set for which the set is closed.   V

Develop an original finite mathematical system by listing a set of elements and by defining an operation on the set for which the set is not closed.   V

Demonstrate whether or not the associative principle holds for any three elements of an original finite mathematical system you have developed.   V

Demonstrate the existence or nonexistence of the commutative principle for an operation on the set for which the set is closed in an original finite mathematical system, and for an operation on the set for which the set is unclosed in an original finite mathematical system.   V

Demonstrate the existence or nonexistence of an identity element for an operation on the set for which the set is closed in an original finite mathematical system, and for an operation on the set for which the set is unclosed in an original finite mathematical system.   V

Demonstrate the existence or nonexistence of an inverse for each element in the set for an operation on the set for which the set is closed in an original finite mathematical system, and for an operation on the set for which the set is unclosed in an original finite mathematical system.   V

Solve problems by using binary operations other than addition, subtraction, multiplication, and division.   III

Solve division of fraction problems by using multiplicative inversion.   III

Recognize examples of the properties of commutativity, associativity, and distributivity.   II

For a given set of numbers and a given operation, recognize whether the operation is closed for that set. II

02-035-030 **Relate the rudiments of logic to mathematics. IV**

Using inductive reasoning (experimental method) as a logical basis for a solution, solve given mathematical problems. III

Using deductive reasoning as a logical basis for the solution, solve given mathematical problems. III

Classify a given problem as an example requiring either deductive or inductive reasoning. II

Classify sentences as either simple or compound. Classify compound sentences as conditional, conjunctive, or disjunctive. II

Derive a conclusion from given premises by use of the "if" rule. III

Write the denial of a given statement. II

Derive a conclusion from given premises by use of the "if-then-not" (IFN) rule. III

Given a simple statement, recognize its denial and the truth value of the denial. II

Given two simple statements, recognize a conjunction and the truth value of a given conjunction. II

02-035-035 **Use the rules of logic to derive conclusions and proofs. III**

Given two simple statements, recognize a disjunction and the truth value of a given disjunction. II

Recognize the antecedent and the consequent of a given conditional, and recognize the truth value of the conditional. II

Using the following laws and definitions, express the reasons for each step in a given completed proof of a numerical statement: definition of natural numbers > 1, commutative laws for + and ×, associative law of identity. II

Using the following rules of inference, derive a conclusion from a given list of premises: rule of adjunction, rule of simplification, rule of expansion, OR rule, IF rule, IFN rule. III

Using the following rules of inference, express the reasons for each step in a completed, logical proof: rule of adjunction, rule of simplification, rule of expansion, OR rule, IF rule, IFN rule. II

02-035-040   Given a problem statement and using standard flowchart symbols, draw a flowchart that shows a logical solution to the problem. III

Recognize flowchart symbols. I

Follow the steps of a given flowchart, stating values that would result if various sets of data were processed. II

02-035-045   Demonstrate that you can use a card punch to enter programs and data on cards. III

Keypunch alphabetic, numeric, and special characters from a prepared list. III

Duplicate the contents of one punched card into another. II

Correct errors that result from improper use of the keyboard. III

From a FORTRAN coding sheet, keypunch an executable FORTRAN program deck. III

02-035-050   **Write simple arithmetic statements in FORTRAN. II**

Demonstrate sufficient knowledge of algebra and FORTRAN to parallel the computer execution of simple arithmetic statements typically found in FORTRAN programs. II

Given a FORTRAN arithmetic statement, identify the following elements: variable, constant, integer mode, real mode, mixed mode. I

Convert a given formula to a FORTRAN arithmetic statement. II

From a flowchart, code simple arithmetic statements that will be included as part of a complete, executable, FORTRAN program deck. II

02-035-055   **Code and execute the FORTRAN solution to a simple problem that requires input by data cards and printed output. III**

Code READ and FORMAT statements to accomplish each of the following. III
1. Read a data card that contains one or more integer values.
2. Read a data card that contains one or more real values.
3. Read a data card that contains both integer and real values.

Code output FORMAT statements that provide either single or double spacing and skipping to a new page before printing a line of output. III

Code WRITE and FORMAT statements to accomplish each of the following. II
1. Write a line of printed output that contains one or more integer values.
2. Write a line of printed output that contains one or more real values.
3. Write a line of printed output that contains both integer and real values.

Write a STOP and an END statement.   II

Code and execute the FORTRAN solution to a problem that requires a single data card and one or more lines of output.   III

02-035-060   Code and execute a FORTRAN solution to a problem that involves branching.   III

Write an unconditional GO TO statement.   II

Write an arithmetic IF statement.   II

Given a computer program containing an arithmetic IF statement and/or an unconditional GO TO statement, predict the sequence of statements to be executed.   III

02-035-065   Given a problem that requires looping, code and execute a FORTRAN solution by using the DO statement and CONTINUE statement.   III

Write a DO statement and a CONTINUE statement.   II

Given a computer program that contains a DO statement, predict the sequence of statements to be executed. III

02-035-070   Code and execute a FORTRAN solution to a problem that requires reading data into an array, array manipulation, and output.   III

Given a description of one or more arrays, write a DIMENSION statement.   II

Write a program that reads data into an array, manipulates its contents, and writes out the array and/or the result of the manipulation.   III

Predict the values resulting from a program that manipulates the contents of an array.   III

02-035-075 Code and execute a FORTRAN solution for problems that require the use of A and X format codes and literal data and the use of the Implied DO technique to read data into and to write from an array. III

Code a READ and a FORMAT statement, using X and A format codes to read a data card. II

Code WRITE and FORMAT statements to accomplish the following. III
1. Write a line of output that contains literal data.
2. Write a line of output, using X and A format codes.

02-035-080 Code and execute a FORTRAN solution to a problem that requires reading data into a multidimensional array. III

Given a description of one or more single or multidimensional arrays, write a DIMENSION statement. II

Write a program that reads data into a multidimensional array, manipulates its contents, and writes out the array and/or results of the manipulation. III

Write a program that utilizes nested DO statements in the processing of a multidimensional array. III

Write a program that utilizes a computed GO TO statement and/or a LOGICAL IF statement. III

02-035-085 Code and execute a FORTRAN solution to a problem that requires the use of a statement function and one or more FORTRAN-supplied subprograms. III

Write a statement function and a statement that requires the use of that function for a given problem. II

Write a statement that uses one or more FORTRAN-supplied subprograms for a given problem. III

02-035-090   Code and execute a FORTRAN solution to a problem that requires the use of a FUNCTION subprogram and a SUBROUTINE subprogram.   III

Predict value(s) returned to a main program from a FUNCTION subprogram or a SUBROUTINE subprogram.   III

Write a FUNCTION subprogram, and write a main program that references the function for a given problem.   III

Write a SUBROUTINE subprogram, and write a main program that calls the subroutine for a given problem.   III

02-035-095   Code and execute a FORTRAN program that involves the following.   III
1. Enter data and print information, using the E, D, and L format.
2. Declare the mode of variables and the size of arrays by using a type statement.
3. Enable a program and a subprogram to share the same computer-storage locations for variables and arrays by using the COMMON statement.
4. Enable variables and arrays within a single program to share the same computer-storage locations by using the EQUIVALENCE statement.
5. Declare a subprogram name as an argument in a subroutine call or function reference by using the EXTERNAL statement.
6. Alter control within a program by using the ASSIGN and the ASSIGNED GO TO statement.
7. Assign values to variables or arrays, using the DATA statement.
8. Temporarily halt a computer program during execution, using the PAUSE statement.

Appendix

Basic Math

02-005-005   Perform the basic operations of addition and subtraction on whole numbers (integers), and solve related word problems.   III

02-005-010   Perform the basic operations of multiplication and division on whole numbers (integers), and solve related word problems.   III

02-005-015   Explain and illustrate the properties of operations.   III

02-005-016   Perform basic operations of addition and subtraction on fractions, and solve related word problems.   III

02-005-020   Perform the basic operations of multiplication and division on fractions, and solve related word problems.   III

02-005-025   Perform the basic operation of addition and subtraction of decimals, and solve related word problems.   III

02-005-030   Perform the basic operation of multiplication and division of decimals, and solve related word problems.   III

02-005-035   Define *ratio* and *proportion,* and use this relationship to solve problems.   III

02-005-040   Find the square root of a given number, and solve related word problems.   III

02-005-045   Find squares and cubes of given numbers, and solve related word problems.   III

02-005-050   Using the four basic arithmetic operations, show that you can solve word problems by using integers, fractions, and decimals.   III

02-005-055   Estimate answers to problems.   III

02-005-060   Use conventional measurements of time, space, and speed accurately, and devise a system for estimating measurements.   V

02-005-065   Convert from one system of measurement to another system.   III

02-005-070   Perform arithmetic operations with measures of size, time, weight, distance, and capacity, and solve related word problems.   III

02-005-075   Trace the development of number systems, and express symbols of one system in symbols of another system.   III

02-005-080   Perform operations on bases other than base ten.   III

02-005-085   Express numbers in expanded and scientific notation.   II

02-005-090   Show your understanding of absolute value.   II

Applied Math

02-010-005   Given a word problem, apply a variety of techniques to help find the solution.   III

02-010-010   Solve problems related to consumer purchases in cash transactions.   III

02-010-015   Solve problems related to consumer purchases that involve time payments, including interest and service charges, and make decisions regarding the total cost of such purchases.   VI

02-010-020   Solve problems related to saving and borrowing money, and make judgments based on your solutions.   VI

02-010-025   Perform procedures related to handling a checking account.   III

02-010-030   Solve problems related to wages, salaries, and commissions and the related deductions.   III

02-010-035   Devise or develop a real or hypothetical family budget, basing expenditures on family size, needs, and desires.   V

02-010-040   Solve problems related to the preparation and serving of food.   III

02-010-045   Solve problems related to decorating and remodeling, and make judgments based on your solutions.   VI

02-010-050   Solve problems related to consumption of utilities in a home.   III

02-010-055   Apply mathematical operations to problems related to your education and career and use your solutions in making decisions.   VI

02-010-060   Make judgments about your insurance needs based on comparative costs and benefits.   VI

02-010-065   Solve problems related to property taxes.   III

02-010-070   Make judgments related to selection of an automobile based on comparative costs.   VI

02-010-075   Plan a trip, using time, cost, and purpose as the basis fo. your plans.   III

02-010-080   Make judgments related to selecting modes of travel based on time, cost, and purpose.   VI

02-010-085   Solve problems related to spectator and participant sports.   III

02-010-090   Plan the redecoration of a room for a customer, considering the customer's budget, needs, and desires.   III

02-010-095   Solve problems related to the handling of money through banks and other lending institutions as related to deposits, checking accounts, and loans.   III

02-010-100   Analyze costs and prices, and use this information in determining profit margin.   IV

02-010-105   Analyze costs and prices, considering discounts and commissions, and use this information to determine profit margin.   IV

02-010-110   Solve problems related to construction of buildings and furnishings.   III

02-010-115   Solve problems related to insurance needs in business.   III

02-010-120   Solve problems related to wages and salaries.   III

02-010-125   Analyze business costs related to the building occupied.   IV

02-010-130   Use rate charts and other given information to make decisions regarding shipping and mailing that are based on time and cost.   VI

02-010-135   Analyze the budget of a given business and recommend possible changes based on income and needs.   IV

02-010-140   Identify key terms related to the operation of computers, and describe their basic functions.   II

02-010-145   Use a slide rule to carry out basic operations and to find squares and square roots.   III

02-010-150   Use a simple hand calculator to solve problems related to business, career, and consumer problems.   III

Geometry

02-015-005   Describe and classify geometric figures by using their properties.   II

02-015-010   Find perimeters, areas, and volumes of geometric figures.   II

02-015-015   Using formulas, solve word problems that require finding the perimeters, areas, and volumes of geometric shapes.   III

02-015-020   Construct and measure geometric figures.   III

02-015-025   Demonstrate and apply the Pythagorean relationship.   III

02-015-030   Apply the Pythagorean theorem, the concept of similar triangles, or trigonometric ratios to make indirect measurements.   II

02-015-035   Apply definitions and properties of angles and triangles to the solution of problems.   III

02-015-040   Apply definitions and properties of lines and planes to the solution of problems.   III

02-015-045   Apply definitions and properties of quadrilaterals and other polygons to the solution of problems.   III

02-015-050   Apply definitions and properties of circles to the solution of problems.   III

02-015-055   Construct deductive and indirect proofs and proofs that use coordinate geometry.   III

02-015-060   Apply knowledge and techniques of coordinate geometry of the line in solving problems.   III

Trigonometry

02-020-005   Apply the definitions, relationships, and theorems of numerical trigonometry to the solution of problems.   III

02-020-010   Derive and use the multiple-angle formulas to prove that an equation is an identity and to solve an equation.   III

02-020-015   Use the definitions of the circular functions and their inverses to graph and to solve analytic problems.   III

02-020-020   Use vectors, polar coordinates, and the polar form of complex numbers to find the solutions to analytic problems.   III

02-020-025   Graph plane curves specified in rectangular or polar coordinates, including those given by parametric equations.   III

02-020-030   Find the derivative of an algebraic, trigonometric, inverse trigonometric, exponential, or logarithmic function, and develop formulas for these and other types of functions.   V

Algebra

02-025-005   Define and use terms appropriate to set notation, and use set theory in solving problems.   III

02-025-010   Use Venn diagrams to represent relationships of sets.   III

02-025-015   Solve simple linear equations and related word problems.   III

02-025-020   Solve simple word problems that involve the basic operations on integers, fractions, and decimals by using algebraic equations.   III

02-025-025   Recognize basic axioms and properties of operations, and use them in solving equations.   III

02-025-030   Develop an original finite mathematical system, defining elements and properties.   V

02-025-035   Perform basic operations on monomials, binomials, and polynomials, and solve related problems.   III

02-025-040   Perform basic algebraic operations and simplifications that include factoring.   III

02-025-045   Solve word problems by factoring polynomials.   III

02-025-050   Solve equations by performing operations that involve algebraic fractions.   III

02-025-055   Use algebraic equations to solve problems that involve ratio and proportion.   III

02-025-060   Apply the rules of radicals and exponents to solve word problems.   III

02-025-065   Identify inequalities and express them through axioms, graphs, or sketches.   III

02-025-070   Solve word problems that involve simultaneous equations.   III

02-025-075   Solve word problems that involve quadratic equations.   III

02-025-080 Solve equations and inequalities that include linear and quadratic systems and polynomial equations.   III

02-025-085 Explain the difference between arithmetic and geometric progression, and solve related problems.   III

02-025-090 Solve problems that require the use of properties of arithmetic, geometric, and binomial expansions.   III

02-025-095 Solve problems that require the use of properties of real numbers or of complex numbers.   III

02-025-100 Classify numbers as rational or irrational.   II

02-025-105 Perform complex algebraic operations and simplifications.   III

02-025-110 Graph relations and functions.   III

02-025-115 Graph truth sets of quadratic equations and inequalities, and graph functions and relations.   III

02-025-120 Graph relations and functions, and find equations of relations and functions, both linear and quadratic.   III

Advanced Math

02-030-005   Use equations and graphs to solve problems related to conic sections.   III

02-030-010   Solve problems by using matrices.   III

02-030-015   Combine principles, concepts, and generalizations by developing an original finite mathematical system, by listing a set of elements, and by defining an operation on the set for which the set is closed and one for which the set is not closed.   V

02-030-020   Solve problems that require the use of properties of exponential, logarithmic, linear, and quadratic functions, and make judgments regarding the efficiency of these functions in given problems.   VI

02-030-025   Find the derivative of an algebraic, trigonometric, inverse trigonometric, exponential, or logarithmic function.   III

02-030-030   Apply knowledge of the properties and functions and limits without reference to calculus.   III

02-030-035   Apply methods of calculus or numerical analysis to the approximation of functional values, transcendental functions, and definite integrals.   III

02-030-040   Derive the integral of an algebraic or transcendental function by using a basic integration formula or a standard technique of integration.   III

02-030-045   Show that you can apply integral calculus to the solution of practical problems from geometry, physics, or everyday life.   III

02-030-050   Apply differential calculus to the solution of practical problems from geometry, physics, or everyday life.   III

02-030-055   Construct derivations or proofs of differentiation formulas or of theorems of differential and integral calculus.   III

Statistics, Probability, Logic, and Computers

02-035-005 Apply the frequencies and measures of central tendency. III

02-035-010 Demonstrate the theory of probability. III

02-035-015 Apply probability theory to solve word problems. III

02-035-020 Express relationships based on sets and set notation. III

02-035-025 Combine principles, concepts, and generalizations by developing an original finite mathematical system, by listing a set of elements, and by defining an operation on the set for which the set is closed and one for which the set is not closed. V

02-035-030 Relate the rudiments of logic to mathematics. IV

02-035-035 Use the rules of logic to derive conclusion and proofs. III

02-035-040 Given a problem statement and using standard flowchart symbols, draw a flowchart that shows a logical solution to the problem. III

02-035-045 Demonstrate that you can use a card punch to enter programs and data on cards. III

02-035-050 Write simple arithmetic statements in FORTRAN. II

02-035-055 Code and execute the FORTRAN solution to a simple problem that requires input by data cards and printed output. III

02-035-060 Code and execute a FORTRAN solution to a problem that involves branching. III

02-035-065 Given a problem that requires looping, code and execute a FORTRAN solution by using the DO statement and CONTINUE statement. III

02-035-070 Code and execute a FORTRAN solution to a problem that requires reading data into an array, array manipulation, and output. III

02-035-075 Code and execute a FORTRAN solution for problems that require the use of A and X format codes and literal data and the use of the Implied DO technique to read data into and to write from an array. III

02-035-080 Code and execute a FORTRAN solution to a problem that requires reading data into a multidimensional array. III

02-035-085 Code and execute a FORTRAN solution to a problem that requires the use of a statement function and one or more FORTRAN-supplied subprograms. III

02-035-090 Code and execute a FORTRAN solution to a problem that requires the use of a FUNCTION subprogram and a SUBROUTINE subprogram. III

02-035-095 Code and execute a FORTRAN program that involves the following. III
1. Enter data and print information, using the E, D, and L format.
2. Declare the mode of variables and the size of arrays by using a type statement.
3. Enable a program and a subprogram to share the same computer-storage locations for variables and arrays by using the COMMON statement.
4. Enable variables and arrays within a single program to share the same computer-storage locations by using the EQUIVALENCE statement.
5. Declare a subprogram name as an argument in a subroutine call or function reference by using the EXTERNAL statement.
6. Alter control within a program by using the ASSIGN and the ASSIGNED GO TO statement.
7. Assign values to variables or arrays, using the DATA statement.
8. Temporarily halt a computer program during execution, using the PAUSE statement.

Index

DATE DUE

GAYLORD

PRINTED IN U.S.A.